Here's what people
An Awakening From The 1
A Journey to En

Anyone who reads the first chapter *of An Awakening From The Trances of Everyday Life*, will be compelled to read the rest.

> C. Norman Shealy, M.D., Ph.D.
> Founding President,
> American Holistic Medical Association

An Awakening From The Trances of Everyday Life is a well-written, easy-to-read, fascinating story full of pearls of pure truth that can set you free to have a most happy and successful life. Highly recommended!

> Vernon Sylvest M.D., author
> *The Formula*

An Awakening is full of sparkling insights and enlightening glimpses into our deep potential. It is overflowing with life truths...a manual of wisdom from nature's book of life.

> Emory John Michael, author
> *Queen of the Sun* and *The Alchemy of Sacred Living*

What a heartfelt empowering modern day parable for adults young and old. It is packed with invaluable teachings for finding balance and harmony in your life. It touched my spirit beyond words.

> Marilou V. Inocalla, M.D.
> Child and Adolescent Psychiatrist

This book is a delight for all ages. The style is easy to follow, the story enjoyable, and the wisdom priceless. I wish I had read it when I was younger.

> David Felder, Ph.D., author
> *How to Work for World Peace*

A delightful book of practical spiritual wisdom for young and old alike.

> Allan Combs, Ph.D., author
> *Synchronicity* and *The Radiance of Being*

Delightful! New analogies with insightful presentation of ancient and basic spiritual knowledge in an amusing, realistic story. The five principles presented and demonstrated through events at Stillpoint one summer will be noted just as the nine insights from *The Celestine Prophecy* gained a mass following. This book is not above anyone's head that can read and it can re-open the window into many souls.

> Robert C. H. Parker
> *New Awareness™Booknews*

This story reaches out to touch our hearts, while stimulating our minds to do the work that allows us to "become conscious of the connection between our individual existence and the sacred fabric" of life. Within the context of a young man's coming to spiritual consciousness readers are gently presented with an understanding of how to connect with our true self, maintain flexible boundaries, choose to create without attachment, and awaken into the awareness of the present moment. In *An Awakening*, Ed Rubenstein has given us a gently enlightening and reassuring tale of recovery and the discovery of one's true self.

> Heidi Rain, writer/book reviewer
> *Spirit of Change Magazine*

An Awakening From The Trances of Everyday Life is timely, reflecting the tumultuous and rapid changes we are experiencing today. Dr. Rubenstein does a superb job penning a rich fabric of wisdom and clarity for all ages to follow. The story is a wonderfully written guidepost for plotting our own inner strength, balance and connection to Spirit.

> Mikaela Rierson, editor
> *The Awareness Journal*

Throughout *An Awakening From The Trances of Everyday Life*, Ed Rubenstein has woven together the most essential and basic elements of the process and journey of self-awareness. The basic tenets explored are well-grounded in the universal principles of life itself: honoring the earth, respecting diversity, faith in a Higher Power, and a reverence for all life. The message is that, indeed, life is a sacred journey.

> Kendall Klug, editor/associate publisher
> *Vision Magazine*

An Awakening From The Trances of Everyday Life is a powerful and inspiring book. Ed Rubenstein has made some universal principles very easy to accommodate, assimilate and integrate into your life by spoon feeding them in a loving way.

> Dr. D. Richard Bellamy, author
> *12 Secrets for Manifesting Your Vision,*
> *Inspiration, and Purpose*

It is filled with depth, intensity and power. Every page is permeated with energy, style, and insight. This visionary novel definitely contributes to society's awakening.

> Patricia Rose Upczak, author
> *Reiki: A Way of Life*

In the vein of Dan Millman's *Way of The Peaceful Warrior,* Ed Rubenstein reveals a journey of a soul that resonates within all of us! It aptly introduces metaphysical concepts including collective consciousness, healing and the self-empowering lesson that we are co-creators with the universe! *An Awakening From The Trances of Everyday Life* is a novel any level student of spirit will enjoy!

> *Pathfinder News*
> St. Louis, MI

Ed Rubenstein sounds a loud and clear wake-up call from the trances of everyday life....You are sure to gain clarity and insight through this remarkable tale of self-realization.

> Paul Fulcher, editor
> *Insight Magazine,* Canada

Ed Rubenstein opens the doors to deep philosophical questions and answers, with an easy-to-read story about a young man receiving life lessons from an elder. Using powerful self-help solutions from today's counseling, spirituality and self-empowerment fields, these lessons are an easy-to-follow route to fulfillment and happiness. This book is written in over 50 bite-sized chapters. Read it all in one evening, or read one chapter a week for a year. Don't let its simplicity fool you. This may be the only self-help book you need this year.

> Nancy Thompson, editor
> *Common Boundary Magazine,* Vancouver

AN

Awakening

FROM THE

TRANCES

OF

EVERYDAY

LIFE

*A Journey
To Empowerment*

ED RUBENSTEIN, Ph.D.

SAGES
WAY
PRESS

Sages Way Press
P.O Box 31
Marshall, North Carolina 28753

Website: www.sages-way.com

ISBN: 09668700-0-X
LCCN: 98-094923

PUBLISHERS CATALOGING IN PUBLICATION DATA

Rubenstein, Edward L., 1953-
        An awakening from the trances of everyday life :
a journey to empowerment / Ed Rubenstein. -- 1st
ed.

        p. cm.
        ISBN: 096687000X

        1. Self-actualization (Psychology)--Fiction.
        2. Spiritual life--Psychological aspects--Fiction
        I. Title.

PS3568.U175A93 1999   813'.54
                            QB198-12263

PCIP Provided By Quality Books, Inc.

Printed in the United States of America
Eerdmans Printing Company, Grand Rapids, Michigan
Cover & Text Design: Linda Grist D'Ville

ACKNOWLEDGMENTS

I am grateful to Marc and Carla San Antonio, whose inspiration and support are behind the birth of this book. Many thanks to Linda Grist D'Ville for her gifted editing, graphic design and creativity, which transformed this book into a polished form. Thank you Joseph Sielinski and Rob Amberg for your photography which appears on the cover. I appreciate Judy Clark for her transcription of the tapes and her patience with my rewrites.

I would like to thank my clients, who have helped me to further explore the concepts that are in this book, as well as contributing to my own learning and growing process.

I express my heartfelt appreciation to the many individuals whose feedback, support, and review of the book has been immensely helpful. This includes Sam Sutker, Sandy Tomlin Sutker, Al Rubenstein, Mike Bowman, Anita Furdek, Steve Lance, Karuna Kistler, Mickie and Betsy Pinkney, Jim D'Ville, Carl and Mary Ann Wilcox, Kate King, Julie Parker and my friends and relatives whose inspiration for this project is present in this book in unseen ways.

I offer my appreciation to my mother, who has been a wonderful model of sincerity, and to my father, whose challenging relationship provided me an opportunity to learn rich and valuable spiritual lessons, as I have come to understand other people's pain.

My deepest affections to my wife, Paramjit, and two sons, Arun and Sage, who have been great teachers and continue to show me that the joy of life shines in their hearts.

My special thanks to Shivananda, Michael Winn and Eng Liang Tan for your mentoring of the Tao.

Lastly, I pay my respects to the Sages of the past, present and future, who show us that human life can be lived with compassion, in balance and harmony.

Ed Rubenstein

*Dedicated
To The
Student And Teacher
Within Us All*

CONTENTS

AN AWAKENING FROM THE TRANCES OF EVERYDAY LIFE

A Journey To Empowerment

1

CONFUSION

"Oh, my God, he's dead!" I wasn't sure whether I wanted to cry, or if I felt relieved. I had to go into the house to tell my mother, "Dad's dead."

My name is Dillon and this is a story of how I woke from the dream of the world — a trance that controlled my thinking, my behavior, my relationships, and my future — a trance that influenced every aspect of my life, and a trance of which I was completely unaware.

A shocking sequence of events took place in my life when I was seventeen. One day, during an argument with my father, I lost my cool. I shouted at him, "Why don't you just drop dead!" I turned and walked away with him still yelling at me. My father had always seemed angry and somehow disappointed with me. He put me down constantly and never had anything encouraging to say.

Two days later my father had a heart attack in our driveway. I ran to him and began doing CPR to the best of my ability. I was giving him mouth-to-mouth resuscitation when I thought I felt him take his last breath. His body went limp as that last breath was released into my own mouth. He was gone. I knelt there, holding his lifeless shoulders, his gray face with blank eyes staring back at me.

A short time after, I began having the same dream over and over again. It seemed so real. I dreamed I was standing at the entrance to our living room. My dad sat on the couch. He was dead, but no one would tell him. He didn't even know it himself. It was my responsibility to tell him he was dead. I was too scared. Every time, just as I

3

was about to tell him, I'd wake up in a cold sweat.

My father was still alive inside of me, it seemed. I could hear his voice in my head telling me I was not good enough, and I believed it. It was as if his voice had become a part of my own voice.

I tried to not think about it and spent my time hanging out with my friends. We were caught up in our own world of partying and never talked about dreams or feelings, or the past. I dared not tell anyone what I was going through. The whole awful scene, and my role in the drama, left me in an internal state of shock.

The few tears I shed were tears of confusion. A part of me felt sad he was dead. Another part of me was glad. What a relief it was that this man I had so greatly feared was out of my life forever. Or so I thought.

I didn't like myself. I didn't like how I felt, or what I saw when I looked in the mirror. I worried about what others thought of me. No one was aware of it because I played a great game and knew how to act cool. Inside, though, I was hurting, and confused. I didn't know who I really was, or what life was about. I just wanted to be liked.

One night I was out with some friends and we were drinking liquor Fred had taken from his father's liquor cabinet. His father was always drunk when I saw him and he never figured out that his son was stealing his booze. We went out for a ride in Fred's Volkswagen Bug. Fred couldn't have walked a straight line, let alone drive a car.

Usually I would sit up front with Fred, and another friend, Bill, would take the back seat. But this time I decided to be a nice guy and give up my front seat to Bill.

There was a green light, but no green arrow. Fred was so drunk he couldn't tell the difference. He made a left turn across the highway without yielding to oncoming traffic. I looked over my right shoulder and saw headlights in my face. The impact of the collision completely crushed the passenger-side door. Time came to a standstill. In an instant I saw everything that had ever happened in my life flash before my eyes. My injuries put me in the hospital for ten days. Bill didn't make it.

By this time, my mother and I were not getting along very well at all. School was out for the summer and she did not approve of the crazy guys I was hanging around with. I tried to explain to her, with them was where I best fit in. I knew she was in pain over the death of my father, and was struggling to work a full-time job to make ends meet. Still, we argued over even the smallest of things.

Late one night it hit me all at once. It was my fault Bill was dead. I had given him my seat. I was tormented by the thought that somehow I was also responsible for my own father dying. The pain was unbearable. I was completely in despair. From somewhere deep in my gut a voice was screaming for help. I cried, "God – who, what and wherever you are, help me! Help me to make sense of all this pain I'm feeling!"

Everything suddenly became very still. It reminded me of the quiet on a snowy day when everything is covered in white. A wave of peace like I had never felt before came over me. A face came into my mind, as crisp and clear as any image could be. It was the face of a white-haired, bearded old man. There were dark streaks in his hair and beard. His eyes were clear and glimmering. His presence was comforting. He smiled and said, "I am Grandfather."

I couldn't believe the games my imagination was playing with me. I wanted to believe this was some kind of sign that maybe something good was going to happen. As the days passed, though, I doubted it more and more. Life went on as usual and I was more confused than ever.

THE WAY IS PREPARED

My mother's growing concern finally prompted her to confide in her friend, Prema, an old woman she'd met at the grocery store. She told Prema about the friction between us, and about my refusal to see a counselor. She explained her fears about the dead-end track I was on, and of the hurt and anger I was trying to hide. The constant worry and physical stress brought about by our arguments was keeping her up nights.

Prema suggested that maybe what I really needed was an opportunity to get away from the city for awhile, and that perhaps spending some time with nature would allow me to get to know myself in a deeper way. She told my mother about a remote cabin in the mountains that she and her husband, Sage, had built for themselves for that very reason.

Sage was getting old, she said, and had been looking for someone to help out with repairs on the cabin. He had postponed his plans to put in some new fences and build a shed because he had not been able to find anyone who was available to work. She suggested to my mother the possibility of my spending the rest of the summer with Sage at the cabin. It would cost me nothing to stay there, she said, and I could even make a little money.

My mother told her I would never agree to such a plan, and that prying me away from my friends would be impossible.

This was on a Friday evening and I was downtown with a group of guys hanging out across from an all-girls' private school. I didn't realize one of the crazy guys in the group was picking a lock and trying to break into a store that was closed for the day. An alarm tripped and everybody ran. Stupid me – when I heard the alarm, I walked over to see what it was.

At that moment, a police car pulled up and a police officer looked me straight in the eye. I knew they would think I had broken into the store. I thought I had better run. Fortunately I can run fast when I'm scared. With every step, though, I had the sickening feeling I was going to be busted for something I hadn't done.

I made it all the way home, but the police were patrolling the neighborhood and I knew they were looking for me. My mother was, of course, surprised to see me home so early and wanted to know what was up. I couldn't bring myself to tell her what had happened, and tried desperately to change the subject. I mumbled something about getting out of town for awhile. What a stupid thing to say! I thought. It was impossible. We couldn't afford any trips, and besides, where else was there to go?

I looked up and saw that my mother had a big smile on her face. It was the first time I had seen her smile in months. Then she told me about Prema and their conversation earlier that evening. It sounded like a crazy idea – hanging out with some old geezer out in the middle of nowhere. But I knew I had no choice. Getting out of town sounded like a good idea, so I agreed to give it a try.

3

ARRIVAL

The next morning Prema stopped by with a map and directions of how to find the cabin, which they had named Stillpoint. I was feeling uneasy after a restless night filled with dreams of cops chasing me. I kept telling them I hadn't done anything, but they chased me anyway.

I threw some clothes in a backpack. I slipped into my mother's car with a hat pulled down over my eyes. When at last we passed through the city limits, I felt a tremendous weight lift from my shoulders. I breathed a huge sigh of relief.

After a few hours of driving, my mother dropped me off at the end of a dirt road. There wasn't a house, or even another person, anywhere in sight. I had to walk up a winding trail to get to Sage's cabin. It was a great feeling walking through the forest. I was alone, and free. No cops would ever find me out here.

It was late afternoon when I approached the cabin. I saw an old man on the front porch sitting in a rocking chair. As our eyes met, I stopped, dead in my tracks. I shook my head in disbelief. There was no denying that Sage was the white-haired old man whose face I had seen when I had cried out to God for help. He even had the black streaks in his gray hair and beard. I began to shake. This can't be, I thought. My mind must be playing tricks on me again.

"Welcome, Dillon," he said. "Grandmother Prema told me you might be coming."

"You're Grandfather Sage," I said.

"Yes, Dillon. Some people call me 'Grandfather.' "

"I had a dream and I thought I saw a face that looked just like you."

"Well, isn't that a coincidence," he said. "I saw you in a dream, and now here you are, right before my eyes."

I wondered if he was making fun of me.

"What should I call you?" I asked.

"You can call me whatever you like."

"How 'bout if I just call you 'Gramps?' "

"That will be fine, Dillon. If I am your grandfather, then that would make you my grandson." He walked over and put his hand on my shoulder. "You know, Dillon," he said, "you are a student of life, just like I am. Welcome to the Stillpoint schoolhouse. Welcome to the classroom of life."

THE CLASSROOM OF LIFE

After a good night's sleep I was awakened by the old man singing a song about how nature is part of his family. I felt at ease listening to him sing, even though it seemed like a scene out of some kind of fairy tale movie. I looked around, but couldn't find a clock.

The cabin was quite primitive. I had been told that Prema and Sage had built it with logs from trees on the land. I went outside to look around. Grandfather Sage had disappeared. There was a large herb and vegetable garden on the south side of the cabin, and beyond that a small orchard. A beautiful river and waterfall flowed nearby.

I'd been used to sleeping in late at home, and realized this would not be part of my routine here with ol' Gramps. He liked to rise with the sun. I sat down on the front porch steps. I wondered if my coming here had been a mistake. There wasn't really much to do. Grandfather came walking up the hill from the river.

"Ready for breakfast, Dillon?" he asked.

He sat in silence for a few minutes before he started eating. I asked him what he was doing and he replied that he was honoring the food, honoring where it came from, and honoring what it was going to do for him. I noticed he did not like to talk while eating. He chewed each bite slowly and embraced each mouthful as if he had never tasted food before.

My habit was to gulp my food down as quickly as possible. I was getting impatient just watching him. He must have known what I was thinking because he smiled and said, "You will get over it."

I grabbed a bunch of grapes and was about to pop a few in my mouth when he stopped me. He suggested that I consider giving thanks to God, and to Mother Earth who nourishes me and provides the food I eat.

I thought things were starting to get a little weird, but decided I would do my best to have an open mind. I decided, too, that I was not going to play games with the old man. I would be honest and tell him how I see things.

"So, Gramps," I asked, when we had finished eating, "what exactly did you mean last night when you said I'm a 'student?' I'm out of school for the summer and I don't intend to do any studying."

"What if I told you we are always in school, wherever we are, and whatever we are doing?" he asked.

"Hey, man, what are you trying to tell me? The whole world is a classroom, or what?" I asked, laughing.

"Exactly, Dillon! Life becomes much more interesting and exciting when you understand that your life itself is your teacher and your classroom."

FALLING IN THE HOLE

It was time to go to work. Grandfather wanted to replace some old fence posts. When we had finished the job a few hours later, he asked me, "Dillon, how would you like me to show you the autobiography of many people's lives?"

"I'm not sure what you mean," I replied.

He asked me to grab a shovel and I followed him down a path about a hundred yards from the cabin. He instructed me to dig a hole about two feet wide and one foot deep. I started digging, wondering what he was up to. He leaned against a tree and closed his eyes while he waited, looking as peaceful as a baby in the arms of its mother. He seemed to be from another planet.

When I had finished digging the hole, he asked me to have a seat where he had been standing.

"You are the audience," he said, " and you are going to see the role that many people play in the theater of life. Are you ready for the first scene?"

"Go for it, Gramps."

He walked down the path and stepped into the hole.

"How did that hole get there?" he asked. Then he stepped out of the hole and walked back to the beginning of the path.

"Now, Dillon. Let me show you the next scene." He walked down the path and stepped into the hole again.

"Why doesn't someone fix that hole?" he asked irritably. In the next scene he walked down the path and fell in the hole again.

"That stupid hole!" he exclaimed loudly. "It should not be there. Who is responsible for this hole in the path?"

He walked over to me then, and said, "This is the condition of many people's lives. They repeat mistakes over and over again. They find fault with others or blame someone else so they do not have to take personal responsibility for their mistakes. They keep falling in the same old hole."

"We all have lessons to learn," he went on, "and we continue to fall into the hole until we have learned the lesson. When we come to realize that falling in these holes is creating pain and misery in our lives, we learn to change."

"I know what you mean, but that doesn't apply to me," I said.

"Let me show you the next scene," he said, walking back to the beginning of the path. This time, he saw the hole, but still fell in.

"It is not always easy to avoid the hole, even when we know it is there. The next scene goes like this." He walked down the path, saw the hole and almost fell in, but then stepped to the side and missed it.

To demonstrate the next scene, he walked down the path and saw the hole way in advance. He walked around it and didn't even come close to falling in.

"Dillon, what do you think the last scene is?" he asked.

I didn't know.

He turned around and took off on a different path. I grabbed the shovel and ran to catch up with him.

"Go back and fill up the hole so we don't fall in again." He placed a hand on my shoulder and stared into my eyes. "With lots of paths, and so many holes, it is important to be able to see where you are walking. Dillon, you are going to learn how to light your path."

6

WE ARE NOT SO FAR APART

L̲ater that day we hiked up a nearby mountain to reach a feeding station Grandfather maintained for the deer in the area.

"Now, Dillon," he said, as we walked, "I would like to share with you a little of my own story. We have more in common than you think."

I could not imagine how I could have anything in common with this old man. After all, he was over seventy years old.

"Dillon, when I was seventeen I was very confused. My father was not a good teacher or role model because he was unsure of the purpose of his own life. He did not know how to give me guidance about how to live a peaceful, balanced life. Like you, I grew up living with fear and intimidation rather than love and support."

"And, like you, I was affected by peer pressure. I compromised my own values, and that got me into trouble. I was told repeatedly that I would never amount to anything. Over time I began to believe it myself and, as a result, I got into even more trouble."

"Many of my friends ended up in jail. They, too, felt that they were not worthy of good things and happiness. They had come to believe the negative messages they were given about themselves. Words like 'you are not good enough' eventually turn into 'I am not good enough.' " He paused, and his normally sparkling eyes became dark and sad. I felt kind of sorry for him.

"I hear you, Gramps," I said. "Those kinds of

messages can be like a tape playing over and over in your head."

"I was fortunate," he continued, "because someone came along who helped me to see those past negative experiences as a gift – a gift that has allowed me to learn, grow and teach others. It was my own pain that helped me to understand the pain that lives in the hearts of so many people."

I didn't know what to say. I thought he was trying to tell me he could feel my pain, yet we hardly knew each other. How could he know anything about my feelings?

7

BUILDING THE FOUNDATION

I was very curious about all the handmade crafts in the cabin. I wondered what was in the antique cabinet next to the woodstove. I opened the cabinet door a couple of inches and peeked inside. Grandfather walked in and caught me.

"Snooping around, eh? Anything I can help you with?"

"Well, I was. . . I mean, I was. . ."

"Cat got your tongue, Dillon? I have a sense you were feeling sneaky and you got caught. Boy, I used to hate it when that happened to me."

I was embarrassed and at a loss for words.

"I. . . I'm sorry," I mumbled.

"I have nothing to hide, Dillon. You are welcome to look around all you like. It feels kind of fun, though, to think you are getting away with something you're not supposed to do, doesn't it? I know what that sneaky feeling feels like. It sure plays with your head."

That evening we built a campfire and sat, staring into the flames for what seemed to be hours. The silence was beginning to get to me and finally I asked Grandfather if he would tell me more about the classroom of life.

"Let's begin with you," he said. "Look at yourself honestly. That means stepping back and observing things like a good sports referee. When you learn to observe your own behavior and witness the results of your actions, you begin to see patterns repeating themselves. Once you learn to recognize these patterns, you can begin developing the necessary skills to create positive changes in your life."

"Hey, wait a minute," I said. "How is it possible for a person to observe his own behavior?"

"Have you ever relived a conversation in your mind and wished you had said something completely different?" he asked. "Do you ever think about past situations and wish you had acted differently?"

"Of course. I do it all the time. I usually wind up kicking myself for saying or doing the wrong thing at the wrong time," I replied.

"Well, then you are already doing it, only you are doing it after the fact," he said. "Now, when you have learned to step back and observe your thinking patterns and behavior as they are taking place," he continued, "you are watching yourself in action. You have an opportunity to create a positive outcome right then and there."

"This takes practice, Dillon. Fortunately, life sees to it that we never run out of material to work with," he chuckled, and got up to put more wood on the fire.

I thought about the events that had led to my coming to Stillpoint, and how things might have been different if I had known how to observe myself in action. If I changed now, how would it affect my life? What would my friends think? I asked Grandfather why it is so difficult for people to change, even though they think the change might be good for them. He asked me what I thought.

"Well, I guess they are afraid of change," I said.

"Yes, fear is part of it. People oftentimes feel safe and familiar with their old ways, even though those old ways create mental discomfort or emotional pain. We may have a fear of letting go because we don't know what will happen when we do. Does a tree fear letting go of its leaves when winter comes? Then, Dillon, why do we fear letting go of old patterns that we have outgrown? Trust that life is on your side and working in your best interest."

That's heavy, I thought. It sounded weird, but I think I knew what he meant because something deep inside me said, "Yes!"

Grandfather stared into the fire for several minutes before he spoke again. "I will share with you, Dillon, five principles which I would like you to consider as the foundation of learning in the classroom of life."

"Number One: Within you there is an inner center where you are at peace and in perfect balance. This inner self is your soul and the essence of who you are."

"Number Two: You have the potential to be in harmony with your inner self. Or, you can block its flow. This will become more clear to you as you learn to study and observe yourself."

"Number Three: You are an active participant in the process of life. You are not a bystander. You are an important part of life, and your life matters just as everyone's life matters."

"Number Four: Your actions and your choices determine the course of your life. The choices you make are directly linked to the life you create for yourself. You are not a victim."

"Number Five: When you cooperate with life, life cooperates with you. In order to flow with the rhythm of life, you must first learn to be in harmony with yourself."

"As you open up to deeper levels of wisdom, you learn to remain in balance and harmony. This means, Dillon, that even if the world around you becomes chaotic, your inner being remains calm. You are not shaken by life's troubles because you are anchored in the truth and essence of your inner center, your soul."

When we returned to the cabin that night, I decided to write down the five principles just in case I ever needed them. They seemed to make sense, but I have to admit I kept asking myself if these principles would actually work in the real world, where I have to focus on defending myself and getting what I want out of life.

8

THE VOICE OF LIFE

After breakfast the next morning we went down to the river with wheelbarrows to collect some stones for landscaping around the cabin.

When we had filled our wheelbarrows, Grandfather sat down and said, "Take a break. Close your eyes."

Over the low roar of the rushing river, I became aware of the more subtle sounds of trickling and bubbling where the water passed between the rocks, which I hadn't heard before. We sat quietly for several minutes. Then Grandfather spoke.

"Life has a voice, Dillon, and it is always speaking to us. When we do not know how to listen, we do not hear."

"What does this voice of life sound like?" I asked, half joking.

"First you must be open, and willing to look, listen and feel. The voice of life manifests as our teacher in many forms. It may speak to you through a particular circumstance or experience. It may speak to you in the form of a person you meet who helps to open your mind or touch your heart."

"Do you mean like you, Gramps?"

"I am honored, Dillon. But I'm not so sure you are even taking my words seriously at this point. I will continue anyway."

"Another example of the way life may speak to us is through things like songs, films or books. Many times in my life books have found me. In other words, I was not consciously looking for the book, but it showed up at the

20

right time, for an important reason. I would read something that would provide an answer to a question I had or a problem I was dealing with at the time. It had something meaningful to say, and that became a gift that life offered me."

"Life also speaks to us and teaches us through our dreams," he continued. "My dreams often speak to me of my unfinished lessons."

"Life may speak to us through other people's pain. We can learn what not to do by studying the painful lessons that others have learned. We can also learn by observing the ignorance others may display. If we do not learn from their ignorance, Dillon, then it may also become our ignorance. When we see others suffer, but we do not learn the lesson, we end up suffering as well. We fall into the same hole that they did."

"I can see that," I said. "I've fallen into the same holes as my friends have."

"The voice of life that often becomes our greatest teacher is our own pain. I am talking about mental and emotional pain. Your pain, Dillon, acts as a signal to inform you that you are not in harmony. It is telling you that you are out of balance. It is important to learn to listen to these messages so you can return to balance and harmony."

"I don't think I have what it takes to listen to those messages," I said.

"Dillon! Wake up! You are in an old hole." Grandfather got my attention and I snapped out of my daze. "What is life telling you now, Dillon?"

"I can't hear anything, Gramps."

"Do you realize your thoughts can create mental discomfort?" he asked. "Listen to the voice of your pain. It is telling you that you are out of balance."

"I guess when I put myself down like that, I'm not in harmony with myself," I said.

"Dillon, if you are not in harmony with yourself, how can you be in harmony with others, or with life? These mental and emotional patterns within you are keeping you out of balance. One of your lessons in life, I feel, is learning to accept and appreciate yourself."

"What's so fascinating to me, Dillon, is the universe has a way of arranging things so that lessons keep reappearing in different forms until we have learned them. We cannot get away from them. Wherever we go, life will be there waiting for us with similar problems and the same lessons to learn."

"Developing insight will help you recognize the gifts of wisdom life is offering you. The first step, Dillon, is learning to recognize when an insight is taking place."

"How do you know when you're having an insight?" I asked.

Grandfather explained that we are to listen for the "ah-ha's" that resonate from our inner center because they are the signals to inform us that an insight is present.

"The next step," he said, "is to understand what the insight means to you personally, and how you can apply it to your life."

I remembered the strong "yes" feeling I'd had the previous night at the campfire. Maybe I had heard the sound of insight. We had been talking about why people fear change, but what does that have to do with me, personally? I wondered.

9

THE SUN AND THE CLOUDS

We were relaxing in the cabin later that day when Grandfather asked me to step outside in order to give him a weather report.

"Dillon, can you tell me if the sun is out?"

"It's cloudy," I replied. "The sun's not out."

He raised his voice and exclaimed, "Look outside again and tell me if the sun is out!"

I went outside. Nothing had changed. What's he getting at now, I wondered. Can't he see the sun isn't out?

"Hey, man, I'm sorry to disappoint you, but not only are there white clouds, there are dark gray clouds," I said. "You can look up at the sky all you want, but you won't get any sun on your face."

He smiled with a childish grin.

"I know that smile," I mumbled to myself. "He's up to something, but what can it be? What is the message here?" I was puzzled.

"Lots of clouds, sunshine not felt," he said.

"That's what I said, Gramps."

"No, it's not Dillon."

"Yes, it is."

"No, it's not."

I started getting angry.

"No, it's not," he said again, laughing.

"Yes, it is!" I insisted.

"Go outside, Dillon, and look again."

I walked out and came back in. "Okay, you win," I said. "Lots of clouds, sunshine not felt."

23

He jumped up and shouted, "You got it, my boy!"

"C'mon, Gramps," I said, still frustrated. "What's going on here?"

"What is the difference between your first report and what you said just now?" he asked. "Go outside, Dillon, and sit quietly. Reflect over what happened and you will realize one of the most important lessons life is offering you."

I went outside and sat on the ground and leaned against a tree. I didn't get it. Grandfather came out and sat down next to me. He closed his eyes. I could see a shining radiance in his face. Wow, I thought. There's a lot of sunshine in him.

Then it dawned on me. The reason he feels so full of light is because he doesn't have clouds blocking his sun. I remembered my first comment — "the sun's not out." Wait a minute. The sun's always out, or we'd be in a lot of trouble on this planet. The sun's always shining, but we don't feel the sunshine when it's blocked by clouds. With light clouds we feel some warmth, but with heavy, dark clouds we feel no sunshine at all.

"I've got it, Gramps," I said. "I understand now."

"You've got it partly," he said, "but not fully. The clouds in your mind did not just blow in from the north or south. If they did, we would all be at the mercy of the wind. This means we would be helpless victims without the power to choose and create. You create the clouds, and you have the power to dissolve them. Do not forget that you create the weather that determines your state of mind. The biggest trap there is, is to think that the clouds just roll in without your being capable of doing anything about it."

"Dillon," he asked, "do you understand how these messages from nature apply to our lives?"

"Well, I think so," I said. "The sun represents my

inner center, where I'm in peace and harmony. The clouds are like the holes I keep falling into, and the negative thoughts in my head. These clouds don't just blow in. The clouds are the patterns of mental discomfort that I create and that I have the power to change. Right, Gramps?"

He looked at me with surprise. "You mean you have actually been listening with an open mind, Dillon?"

"I hear it and I understand it," I replied. "It's a great way to live, out here in the woods, but I'm not so sure it would work in my world."

10

THE GARDEN

The next morning we spent a few hours working in the vegetable garden, which supplied us with much of our food.

"Dillon, as we stand in this garden now, the voice of life is speaking to you," said Grandfather.

My first thought was that the spinach and lettuce didn't have much for brains. Grandfather winked at me. He knew just how to read me, it seemed.

"To be honest, I'm not sure what the connection is between me and your garden except that it gives us food to eat," I said.

"Dillon, the voice of life is providing us a crucial piece of the puzzle regarding the relationship of this garden and the workings of our minds. If we look, feel and listen, we can grasp the wisdom the garden offers us."

He asked me to sit with him in the center of the garden, to be silent and observe what was going on there. The garden was filled with a variety of vegetables. Some vegetables had ripened. In other parts of the garden seeds had recently been planted and the soil was still bare of vegetation.

"What do you observe, Dillon?"

"I see vegetables and I see bare land," I replied.

"Those bare patches in the garden have been planted with seeds and will soon bear fruit. What does the voice of life show us here?"

"Well, seeds are planted. They eventually sprout and grow into the vegetables we eat. Tomato seeds give you tomatoes and broccoli seeds give you broccoli."

"What else, Dillon? Explain to me the connection between this garden and your mind."

I stared out across the garden. "I don't see any connection." I said.

"Dillon, let's say your mind is the garden. In the garden of your mind, what are the seeds?" he asked.

"I'm not sure," I said.

"Thoughts are the seeds. What is the fruit in the garden of your mind?" he asked.

Now I was totally confused. "I don't know, Gramps."

"Feelings, Dillon, are the sprouts that come forth from the seeds of your thoughts. As you sow in the garden of your mind, that shall you reap in the fruits of your feelings."

"I never thought about my mind being a garden," I said.

"Different seeds bear different fruit," said Grandfather. "Broccoli seeds will give you broccoli, and poison ivy seeds will give you poison ivy. Dillon, what does this have to do with the garden of your mind?"

"I guess it means the type of thoughts I think, or plant in my head, are directly connected to the type of feelings I have."

"Another way to put it, Dillon, is crappy thoughts produce crappy feelings. Positive thoughts bear positive fruit."

When we had finished weeding and watering the garden we picked some lettuce and other greens to make a salad for lunch.

"Dillon, what happens if you, the gardener, fail to weed your garden?" Grandfather asked.

"I guess the weeds would take over, Gramps."

"I have had a lot of weeds that took me quite a while to get under control," he said. "Sometimes you think you've gotten rid of a certain type of weed and the next thing you know, it creeps back into your garden. The idea, Dillon, is to recognize those weeds and deal with them when they are young sprouts, or before you know it they are developing a root system and it takes a lot of energy and work to clear them out of your garden."

I thought I felt an "ah-ha." I knew he was talking about the garden of the mind.

"Before I met you, Gramps," I said, "the weeds in my mind were six feet high and I couldn't find any good vegetables to eat."

He laughed.

It was encouraging to hear even Grandfather had weeds that occasionally cropped up in his garden.

11

THE BIRD'S NEST

After lunch we walked a short distance through the woods to a beautiful, still pond situated near an open meadow. The surrounding area was a bird sanctuary, he told me. He shook one of the trees and a number of birds began flying overhead.

"What is the voice of life communicating to us now, Dillon?" he asked.

I didn't have the foggiest idea. "Birds fly, and I can't fly," I said.

Grandfather laughed. "What are the birds showing you?" he asked.

"They are showing me they can fly," I replied.

"Yes, Dillon. They can fly. And where are they flying?"

"The birds are flying over our heads."

"That is correct, Dillon, and what conclusion can you come to from this observation?"

"I'm stuck on this one, Gramps."

He got a very serious expression on his face and looked straight into my eyes. "You may not be able to keep a bird from flying over your head," he said, "but you can sure prevent it from building a nest in your hair."

We both burst out in laughter.

"How did you expect me to figure that one out?" I asked.

"I didn't, Dillon. But maybe we can translate this experience into a useful insight."

My mind began to race looking for an answer.

"You will not get the answer from your intellect. We will sit in silence until you get it. Allow your inner voice to tell you," he said.

We sat down and after a while I began to worry because nothing was coming to me. I knew he would be willing to sit there until midnight, if necessary. He loved his silence. I became increasingly impatient.

"I don't think you are going to get it by sitting there squirming," said Grandfather. "I suggest you be still and look inside, and the insight will be revealed to you."

Thoughts of different sorts poured into my mind. I let them go and continued to sit quietly. Then some thoughts about the guy who had wrecked my bike came into my mind. I felt anger brewing inside of me. I became aware of the negative thoughts and the feelings of anger I was creating. I realized there was no changing what had happened, and I let it go. All of a sudden, it seemed a light bulb flashed on. Ah-ha! The voice of life spoke to me.

"I got it! The birds represent your thoughts. You may not be able to keep negative thoughts from passing through your mind, but you can sure prevent them from building a nest in your head."

"Yes!" Grandfather said, with a radiant smile. "You got it!" He explained that self-defeating thoughts that nest in your head are like the weeds that can get out of control in the garden of your mind.

"Dillon, we are human. Self-defeating thoughts will come and go. The question is whether or not you invite them in, give them a bed to sleep in and food to eat."

"I guess we don't want them to get so comfortable they don't want to leave."

"Exactly, Dillon."

We laughed again.

12

CONTENTMENT

It rained that night and most of the next day. Grandfather kept busy in the cabin – first, chopping vegetables to make a pot of soup, then wiping down all the shelves in the kitchen, then repairing the handle on an old garden rake.

He brought out a collection of arrowheads he had found in the area to let me look at them. One arrowhead in particular caught my eye. I could make a necklace out of it when I got back home, I thought. I slipped it into my pocket. I was sure he would never miss it, considering how many he had.

Grandfather finally settled in his rocking chair in front of the woodstove with a book. I had put the arrowhead collection away and had looked through all the magazines in the cabin by then. I sat staring out the window at the rain.

The forest looked beautiful, with a foggy mist moving gracefully through the treetops. Still, I couldn't help wondering when the rain might stop. Grandfather looked up and set his book aside.

"You know, Dillon, life will never be perfect if you judge it in terms of how things are looking on the outside. Contentment is a state of mind and it is your responsibility to discover how to experience it."

"The world, in many ways, is a mess," he continued, "and probably always will be. People do stupid things. New things get old and they break. Even in nature things are not perfect. Too much sun, you burn. Bee stings hurt, thorns prick. The world cannot give you contentment. If you do not find the sweetness of contentment on the inside, then the outside world looks sour. But when you learn to experience contentment within, you can enjoy the world because you do not expect your happiness to come from the world."

"Dillon, do you realize you have been brainwashed by society?"

"What do mean by 'brainwashed?' " I asked.

"You can think of it as a conditioning process. And some of this conditioning has been good. That means it supports and nourishes the development of the positive you."

"I know what you're getting at now, Gramps. You're saying I've also been negatively conditioned, and it's interfering with my ability to be content within."

"That's right, Dillon. And it is often convenient to blame someone or something else in your life for your not being happy or content. These excuses are a cop-out. When we use excuses, Dillon, we are forgetting that we, ourselves, are responsible for being content within."

"I think I know what you mean. I used to blame my father for just about everything. After he died I started blaming my mother, or the school, if things didn't turn out right."

"The mistake people often make," said Grandfather, "is they look to achieve happiness from external things. That's a trap."

I looked out the window again and thought about the values of my peer group. I asked myself, "Where do my friends think happiness comes from?" It was very clear that sex and money are the things they feel they must have in order to be happy. I explained this to Grandfather.

"Do you believe that, Dillon?" he asked.

"Well, yes, I guess I've thought the same thing, but it does sound kind of funny."

"Yes, Dillon. Sex and money are the cosmic joke. Depending on them for contentment will send you on a wild goose chase. There is no saying where that ride could lead you, but one thing is sure – it is a dead end road. People have been falling in that hole and getting themselves in trouble throughout the history of humankind."

"Do not buy into the negative conditioning that tries to tell you success is what you have or possess. True success is based upon what you are inside. Your quality of life, Dillon, depends upon the quality of your mind."

He picked up his book again. I continued to sit quietly, watching the trees through the window. I felt guilty as I fingered the arrowhead in my pocket.

13

BEING FLEXIBLE

The rain stopped late in the afternoon. We went for a hike and stopped to rest in an area that had been hit quite hard by a storm the previous winter. Grandfather asked me to look around and tell him what I saw. I observed many trees broken off or lying uprooted on the ground.

"There is a lesson here to learn," he said, and asked me if I could discover the insight. "Your hint, Dillon, is to closely study the fallen trees, and then study the trees still standing. Why is it that certain trees survived the storm while others did not? Is that just a coincidence?"

I wandered through the forest comparing the trees. I noticed the trees that had toppled over had shallow root systems. Those trees that were rigid, and not able to bend and flow with the storm, were snapped in half. The trees which were well-rooted and flexible were able to bend and adjust to the weather conditions.

"I guess we're supposed to live our lives like the trees that are still standing – being strong, flexible and well-rooted," I said.

"This is true, Dillon, and it is good to be rooted as long as you are rooted in goodness and good will. Be committed to your foundation which you come to know as your truth. But be flexible as well, because change may call you to a better way, and if you are rigid, you miss out. When you are flexible, you bounce back when the storms of life hit you. When you are rigid, you break easily."

I thought about what Grandfather said regarding

the importance of being well-rooted. I remembered how, so many times, I had casually gone along with whatever my friends wanted to do. If I don't learn to be anchored, I thought, I will be influenced again and again, and the storms of life will blow me over. I felt unsure about my ability to change.

Grandfather sensed my concern. "Lighten up and enjoy the ride," he said. "Storms will come and go. It is an inevitable part of the nature of life. People will disappoint you at times. You will see the acts of other people's ignorance, and their ignorance may affect you or your loved ones. Not only that, your ignorance may affect others at times."

"Give the world permission to be imperfect," he continued. "Expect goodness, but understand that difficult things can happen. Guess what, Dillon? There will be many times when you get knocked down, or thrown from the horse, so to speak."

"What do you do then?"

"Do you want to lose your horse, Dillon?"

"No."

"Then what might you choose to do?"

"I better brush myself off and get back on the horse," I said.

"Exactly, and that is just what you do in life. A spiritual warrior is not afraid to be knocked down because he knows he will brush himself off and rise again. Dillon, I have another secret for you. When you fall off the horse, or you get knocked down, there is always a gift waiting for you."

"You are given the opportunity to strengthen your character," he continued, "and to learn something about yourself, or about life, that you may not have known. That is the gift. Could it be that you allowed yourself to be thrown from the horse? It is important to examine this new information you have received, and learn from it, so it does not happen again."

"Are you saying, Gramps, that obstacles can be our friends? I have a problem with that. I see them as a pain in the ass."

"If we treat obstacles as our enemies, life will be an uphill battle. If you greet obstacles as challenges, you can have fun even when the going gets rough."

"That's easier said than done, Gramps."

"Dillon, you are absolutely correct. I choose to keep reminding myself, though, that obstacles are my challenges and my friends. I have had a tendency to sometimes forget this, especially when I am in the middle of them," he said, laughing at himself. "I make it sound easy, perhaps, but believe me, Dillon, my life has been a challenge and it has taken perseverance to reach my present level of understanding. Be patient and do your best to enjoy the ride."

"I hear what you're saying, and it makes some sense," I said, "but I still think you're out to lunch about how problems can be your friends."

"Maybe so, maybe not, Dillon. But since they are inevitable, why not adopt a positive way of looking at them?"

14

THE COCOON

On our way back to the cabin, we stopped at a raspberry patch and ate berries as we plucked them from the bushes.

"These berries are great."

"I appreciate them, too, Dillon. Sometimes, to get to the sweetest berry, you have to get around the thorns. Watch where you are going."

"I know, Gramps. Some of the thorns of life have caught me in the butt because I wasn't watching where I was going."

Grandfather pointed out a cocoon. "What would happen if you opened up that cocoon?"

"I guess we'd see a caterpillar."

"Would it serve that caterpillar if we opened up its cocoon?"

"No. It wouldn't have a chance to become a butterfly."

"That's right, Dillon. Did you know if you do not let a baby fall when it is learning to walk, it does not learn to walk as well?"

"I think I understand what you're saying. The energy the caterpillar exerts to break open the cocoon gives it the strength to metamorphose and fly away as a butterfly."

"Likewise, Dillon, our lives are a metamorphosis."

"So, you think you can fly, Gramps?" I laughed.

"Yes. And you are already learning to fly. You just don't know it yet. Let your challenges give you greater strength and stamina. You will know you have earned your wings when you learn to live in the world, without being caught up in the soap opera."

We headed back to the cabin as the sun was starting to set. On our way we passed by a muddy pond.

"Do you see that lily in the pond?" asked Grandfather. "It's in the mud, but its blossom is well above the mud, basking in the sun."

"I see it," I said. "Sometimes getting muddy is fun though, ya know."

"It's your life, Dillon. Play it as you choose."

We walked on, but I couldn't get his last statement out of my head. I get to play life as I choose. The arrowhead in my pocket began to feel very heavy. I couldn't believe how guilty I felt. Is this really the way I'd like to play this scene? My guilt feelings seemed to overpower the pleasure I'd felt in possessing the arrowhead. I decided it wasn't worth it.

Later, back at the cabin, when Grandfather stepped outside to get some firewood, I cautiously slipped the arrowhead back in with the rest of the collection.

15

I NEED WHAT?

The next day we went down to the river to cool off after a few hours of working in the hot sun.

"Dillon, is there anything you need?" Grandfather asked.

"Sure. I need a new bike and some new sneakers, and I need..."

"That's enough, Dillon."

He asked me to bend down and put my head under the water. I thought he was challenging me to see how long I could hold my breath and stay under. I took several deep breaths to build up my lung capacity, then went under.

After about fifty seconds I was running out of air and started to raise my head to the surface. I felt a hand behind my head, holding me down. I started to freak out. Is he trying to kill me? I wondered. "I need air!" I cried out in my mind. He released his hand from my head and I burst up, gasping for air.

"What are you?? Nuts?" I yelled. "You could have killed me!"

"Do you need air?" he asked calmly.

"What's your point?" I asked.

"You cannot live without that which you need, Dillon."

Here we go again, I thought. What is this guy getting at now? He sure has a strange way of making a point.

"So we agree that you need air," he continued. "Do you need a bike? And sneakers?"

"Well, not exactly, I guess."

"If you do not need them, then what is your relationship to that bike?"

"I'd like to have a new bike," I said.

"Exactly! Do not confuse needs with luxuries. A bike and sneakers are luxuries, not needs. What you would like and what you need are very different. You need air, water, food, and shelter, or you cannot survive. When you do not have your needs met, you feel threatened, just like you did when you ran out of air under the water."

We climbed up the bank from the river and headed back to the cabin for lunch.

"Dillon, how would a meal taste if we used weeds instead of fresh garden vegetables?"

"I know where you're going with this story, Gramps," I replied. "You're saying in the garden of the mind there are weeds, and the term 'I need' is one of them."

"Dillon, you're no fun," he laughed. "I thought I was going to get to play a while longer, but you cut straight to the point. Yes, you are correct. When you think you need something, you create a feeling that something is wrong if you do not have it. Have you ever experienced that?"

"Well, it reminds me of a girl I met last winter. I felt like I really needed her to go out with me. I asked her to go out on a date, but she turned me down. When she said 'no,' I thought I would die. It felt devastating, like my world had fallen apart."

"Your world did fall apart. You created a drama that said, 'I need her to like me and go out with me.' Your 'need' created a sense of disaster when it did not happen. Your world also started falling apart when your head was under the water, didn't it?" he asked.

"Yes, it did. Real quick!"

"The difference is you really did need air, and in a few more seconds, if you did not get any, we would have had a serious crisis on our hands," he laughed.

"I didn't think it was very funny at the time."

"Your need for air was real. Your need for that girl was your self-created illusion. You needed her like you needed a hole in the head."

"It took me a while to get over it. I finally told myself I didn't need her. Everything seemed to get better after that."

"Exactly, my boy. You cancelled the need. You filled in the hole you had dug."

"What else could I have said, instead of 'I need her to go out with me?' "

"How about 'it would be nice if she goes out with me, but if she chooses not to, so be it.' How does that sound?"

"It's sure better than thinking 'I need her.' "

"You can hope she goes with you, and that's okay. Just do not get needy, or you set yourself up. That poor girl missed out on the opportunity to get to know you. Boy, did she blow it."

"I like that better," I said. "So instead of saying 'I need,' I can substitute it with 'I would like.' "

"Exactly, Dillon. Or you can say 'I prefer.' If what you are hoping for does not happen, your world is still intact. You maintain your balance."

16

LIGHTNING

After an early supper that evening I felt restless and told Grandfather I was going to hike out into the woods and do a little exploring. He warned me that if I ventured into the forest beyond the feeding station there would not be any more trails. He suggested I take his compass, or I might have trouble finding my way back. I laughed.

Who does he think he is, to think I don't have enough common sense to find my way back? I thought. I took off, and when I reached the end of the trail I thought if I hiked for just a few more minutes I could easily find my way back.

It was incredibly refreshing to be out on my own for a change. I walked into a grove of ancient-looking trees and sat down to rest. My mind wandered back to the city, and my friends. I smiled, wondering what they'd say if they could see me now. A rolling of thunder in the distance brought me back to the present. I decided to head back.

I stood up and saw dark clouds moving in. I heard thunder again and saw a flash of lightning. It started to rain. I started running back toward the cabin. The thunder sounded like a bowling alley. I could feel it shaking the ground as I ran.

It began raining harder. I ran until I was out of breath, then ducked under a tree to rest for a moment. I looked around and suddenly realized I should have been back to the feeding station by this time. *I had been running the wrong way!!*

I started to get scared. Lightning was flashing all around me. I curled up in a fetal position under the tree and put my arms over my head. I had never been more frightened in my life.

The rain and lightning storm lasted for what must have been hours. It eventually settled down to a hard steady drizzle, but by then it was pitch black. I was cold, wearing only a t-shirt and shorts, which were soaking wet.

I could hear coyotes howling from somewhere in the distance. I thought I heard wild animals nearby, but I couldn't see a thing in the darkness. I was petrified with fear. I thought I would either be eaten, or shiver to death from the cold. It was the longest night of my life.

I was so relieved when the sun began to rise I actually thanked God for letting me live. I got up and started running. Even though I didn't know where I was going, it made me feel less like I was lost. I began to warm up as I ran. Eventually I came to a dirt road. I followed it, and within a short distance, recognized it as the main road that lead to Grandfather's trailhead.

When I got back I found Grandfather sitting on the porch in the morning sun, peeling an apple.

"I guess you forgot to take the compass," he said, smiling.

"Very funny, Gramps. You've got a weird sense of humor."

"I am glad you were not eaten, Dillon. The mountain lions are hungry this time of year. If you had not shown up by eight this morning, I was going to have a search and rescue squad go looking for you. I'll bet you were scared up there in that lightning storm, having to spend the night in the wilderness and all."

"It wasn't too bad," I said. "I actually had a pretty good time."

"I'm glad to hear that, Dillon. I was concerned you may have been frightened."

"I'm tougher than you think, Gramps."

"I guess I didn't realize how tough you are, Dillon."

17

FIGHT OR FLIGHT?

Later that morning Grandfather suggested we go into the woods to track some animals. "Not to hurt them, Dillon, but to study them," he said. "Your task is to observe how an animal reacts when you do your very best to catch it."

Going back out into the woods was the last thing I wanted to do, and I had a hunch he was well aware of it. I didn't have the nerve to say anything though, and got ready to go.

After an hour or so of hiking, we came to a small clearing. On a nearby hill we could see a couple of deer grazing. As we approached, they sensed our presence. One of the deer looked over her shoulder at us, and they both took off as if they were running for their lives.

We resumed our hike, and several minutes later Grandfather asked me, "What do you think those deer are doing now?"

"They are most likely grazing on the other side of the hill," I said.

"Exactly, Dillon."

Next we saw some wild turkeys. When we tried to go near them, they took off like they thought they were going to end up on somebody's Thanksgiving table.

"I never knew a groundhog could move so fast until I tried to catch one," said Grandfather. "What is going on with these animals, Dillon?"

"They feel the need to escape."

"What would happen if we cornered them, and they

could not get away?" he asked.

"I guess they would put up a pretty good fight, even to their death."

"Yes, they would. Do you know what this response is called, Dillon?"

"It's the survival mechanism."

"Right. Another name for it is the fight/flight response. When animals are faced with danger, they either fight or take flight. One of two things happens: they either lose the fight and die, or they get away. If they get away, what do you think they do next?"

"Well, Gramps, I don't think they're getting an ulcer wondering if we're on their trail."

"That's right. Dillon, is this survival mechanism bad or good?"

"It's good."

"Actually it can be both," he said.

"I remember my own survival mechanism kicking in one time," I said. "Last year a group of older guys gave me a hard time and embarrassed me in front of my friends. Some months later, it snowed. I was sort of showing off, and threw a snowball across the street with all my might. Unfortunately, one of those guys got his head in the way and the snowball creamed him. He fell to his knees for a moment, and I knew his brain must have been in shock. Boy, was he pissed. He came running over with a group of five big guys, more angry than a bat out of hell. I froze. One of my friends yelled, 'Run!' I took off. They chased me, but they couldn't catch me. I ran faster than I ever have in my life. I jumped over a fence I never believed I could have cleared. If it wasn't for that fight/flight response, I would have been hurting pretty badly. That's why I think the survival mechanism is good. It saved my life."

"Dillon, my survival mechanism has also saved me several times in my life. It also gave me the strength to help save others when the need arose. This is the good part of the survival mechanism. It is surely there for an important reason."

"I know you told me," he went on, "that spending the night out in that lightning storm was no problem, but are you sure your fight/flight response wasn't activated even just a little bit?"

"Well, maybe a little," I replied.

"That's funny, because when I tuned in to you last night, I could have sworn your heart and mind were racing."

I wondered if he was playing games. Or could he really "tune in" to me?

18

AM I REALLY BEING THREATENED?

When we returned to the cabin we saw two rabbits munching on lettuce in the garden. I started toward them to chase them away, but Grandfather stopped me.

"There is enough to feed the four of us," he chuckled. We sat down on the front porch steps to watch them while we rested from our hike.

"Dillon, why do you think God installed all those animals, and you and me, with a survival mechanism?"

"So we could survive."

"When does our survival mechanism become activated?" he asked.

"When we feel threatened," I replied.

"Exactly, Dillon, but there are different degrees of activation of this mechanism."

"You mean at times we may feel only a little threatened, and other times we may feel extremely threatened?" I asked.

"That's right. This is a biological mechanism involving an alteration of your brain chemistry and endocrine glands. There are multiple changes your body goes through when your survival mechanism begins to activate, such as constriction of your arteries and changes in your brainwaves."

"Why would your arteries constrict during the fight/flight response?" I asked.

"That is a good question. When our distant ancestors were in danger, it may have been because their tribe was under attack, or they were battling the elements.

48

If they were badly cut, it was important for the smooth muscles that surround the arteries to tighten so that the arteries could constrict. This way, they did not bleed to death."

"That makes sense," I said. "When you're relaxed, the arteries are more open, or dilated."

"Yes, that is how it works. In fact, it is quite easy to learn the art of dilating your arteries."

"How can you tell when they're dilated?"

"When they are dilating, there is increased blood flow, allowing more volume of blood to pass through the arteries. When your external temperature is rising, it means the arteries are dilating. When you get uptight, the arteries begin to constrict and your temperature drops."

"Did you know," Grandfather continued, "you can control this dilating process simply by using your own intention? You can raise the temperature of your hands, for instance, by ten degrees or more."

He got up to get a thermometer and some tape from the cabin. He taped the thermometer to the tip of my index finger. He told me to remain relaxed, but with the intention of allowing my hand to get warmer. That means, he said, to simply state your intention and then step aside and allow it to happen.

It took me a while, at first, to understand what 'allowing' meant. I really wanted to see how this worked, but the temperature would not change. Grandfather said I was trying too hard. He reminded me of the conversation we'd had the previous day about the problems that arise when you create a need in your mind.

I looked up at the rabbits for a moment, and let my mind go blank. Finally I was able to let go of the need to make it happen. I looked down at my hand. It began to tingle and feel warmer. I observed those feelings, and before I knew it, my hand temperature went up eleven degrees. It had started out at 84, and was now at 95 degrees.

"Now, Dillon, can you step into the shoes of that scared young man who just realized he hit a bully in the head with a snowball?"

Within seconds, I began to feel the fear I had felt on that day. My heart started to speed up and I got a knot in my stomach.

"What happened after the snowball hit him, Dillon?"

"I ran fast."

"What was that like?"

"Like running for your life," I said.

He asked me to look at the thermometer. To my surprise, the temperature had dropped back down.

"That's amazing! I ran from those guys over a year ago, but my biology still responds to that memory."

"Good insight, Dillon!"

"What's also amazing is inside I felt threatened again, even though I'm sitting here with you in complete safety."

"The main point," said Grandfather, "is that just because you feel defensive, or threatened, or unsafe, does not necessarily mean you are actually in danger. Now, those feelings may be there for a good reason. You or someone else may really be in danger. Your house could be on fire, there could have been a car wreck, a tornado is nearby, you're being attacked, or you have to run fast to help someone. These are good reasons for your survival mechanism to be activated, and that is what it is designed for. The fight/flight response helps us to help ourselves, or others, during very difficult or threatening circumstances."

"Well, Gramps, the deer also ran for a good reason.

They have probably seen many of their buddies get bumped off by hunters."

"That's right, Dillon. But when the danger is eliminated, they go back to grazing."

"I think many humans have forgotten how to graze," I said.

"Absolutely. Many people go about with their survival mechanism activated at all times, as if they are being hunted. Low self-esteem, worrying or feeling unsafe in relationships can keep this fight/flight response activated."

"Is it because so many people have been conditioned that way?"

"Yes, that is part of it."

"I think I've spent most of my life with my fight/flight response partially activated because I haven't felt safe and secure in my surroundings," I said.

"You are probably right, Dillon. It is not a full-blown activation of the fight/flight response, but a constant simmering. That is the sad story of so many people's lives. Why do they not even know they feel unsafe?"

"Maybe they've never known what it feels like to be safe," I replied.

"Yes. And the quality of their lives suffers as a result. You cannot be content when you are walking around with an activated fight/flight response. You miss out on the joy of life."

I thought about how I could have used the hand-warming exercise to relax and warm my body the previous night out in the storm.

"That hand-warming exercise can sure come in handy if you are ever lost in the woods," said Grandfather.

19

I CHOOSE

"I have some more thoughts I would like to share with you regarding the way you speak to yourself," Grandfather said, as we were doing the dishes that night.

"We all talk to ourselves, don't we?" I asked.

"Of course we do. This is called self-talk. As we discussed earlier, thinking or saying 'I need' creates desperation when you do not get that which you think you need. The stronger your attachment to that which you think you need, the stronger the emotional reaction when you do not get it or have it."

"Saying 'I need' can create an arousal of your fight/flight response. Right, Gramps?"

"That is correct, Dillon. Can you figure out some other self-talk that can be weeds in the garden of your mind?"

"You mean like clouds that block the radiance of the sun?" I asked, laughing.

He grinned back at me. "Yes, I'm talking about those word phrases that interfere with your ability to be in harmony with yourself. Let's see if we can discover some seed patterns from your past that have caused you agitation."

I thought back to a time last spring when I was feeling overwhelmed with homework and chores around the house.

"What did you say to yourself, Dillon?"

"I said, 'I have to get this done. I've got to do it and I should do it now.' "

"Those words create agitation, Dillon, because it makes you feel you are facing a desperate situation. You end up motivating yourself into action through guilt, as if you are whipping yourself into gear. Is it a nice way to live when you are motivating yourself into action because you've 'got to,' 'have to,' 'must' or 'should?' "

"No. But if you have to do something, or it must be done, then you've 'got to' do it, don't you?"

"Dillon, you are free to think however you like, though I will point out to you there are consequences to the words and thoughts you use in communicating with yourself. There is no need to beat yourself up unnecessarily."

"How else can you talk to yourself about things like that?" I asked.

"Dillon, I will share with you one of the most empowering words in our language. You can add it to your everyday method of talking to yourself."

"Don't keep me in suspense," I joked. "What is this empowering word?"

"Dillon, repeat after me: I choose to do it now."

"I choose to do it now," I said.

"How does that feel compared to 'I've got to do it now' or 'I should and must do it now?' I know it sounds simplistic, Dillon, but if you work with this word, you will find it to be quite profound and life changing."

"I can see how 'I choose' feels empowering," I said. "It feels as if it comes from a solid and deep place inside of me."

"It does, Dillon. Now repeat, 'I choose not to do it now,' or 'I choose to address that later.' How does that feel?"

"When I use the words 'I choose' or 'I choose not to,' I don't feel the agitation I felt with the other words," I said.

"Dillon, when you choose to choose, you are in the driver's seat. When you 'should' do it, it is as if someone is making you do it. That ruins the fun. Whether it be cleaning the toilet, doing dishes or homework, if you've 'got to,' 'have to,' 'must' or 'should,' a part of you resents it. When you 'choose' to do it, you can enjoy doing what you have chosen. Dillon, washing dishes or doing laundry, and even doing your homework can be enjoyable if you are doing it through a sense of choice rather than feeling you are being forced to do it."

"I can choose not to do something, too," I said.

"That is correct. You accept responsibility that choosing not to do something can have consequences and you earned them."

"I guess we can choose not to do the dishes, but the consequences may be we get rats in the kitchen," I said. "I remember times when I hated doing my chores because I thought, I 'have' to do them. Maybe I'll 'choose' to do my chores."

"Dillon, I guarantee your chores will be more fun now that you do them by choice."

20

A DONE DEAL IS A DONE DEAL

One morning as we were just about to begin some repair work on the roof of the cabin, Grandfather suddenly changed his mind.

"What a beautiful morning!" he exclaimed. "Life is speaking to us from every direction! I believe I hear the birds calling us down to the river. Let's go, Dillon!"

We put our tools away and walked downstream until we came to a shady spot where a beautiful green moss covered the rocks like a plush carpeting. We sat on the ground where we could feel rays of sunshine through the branches of the trees, warming our skin.

Grandfather got up and walked away. He returned a few minutes later with a dead butterfly and a dead ladybug he had found.

"Open your hand, Dillon. I would like you to hold these." He placed the butterfly and the ladybug in my palm.

"What would you like me to do? Bury them?" I asked.

"I would like you to bring them back to life."

"How can I do that? They're dead."

"Go ahead. Try, and see what happens."

"I can try from now until doomsday, Gramps, but this butterfly is not going to fly out of my hands."

"Why is that?" he asked.

"Because it's a done deal. They're dead."

"I agree, Dillon. A done deal is a done deal. Would it make sense to argue with a done deal and expect the circumstances to change?"

"Well, you could, Gramps, but you'd be wasting your time. Why argue or try to change a done deal? Why try to bring something back to life that's already dead?"

"Exactly. I have a question for you, Dillon. Have you ever said to yourself, 'That shouldn't have happened,' or 'They shouldn't have done that to me?' "

"Well, sure. I have said that a number of times when things happen that I don't like."

"Guess what you are doing."

"I'm not sure." I reflected on the time someone had put nails in my tires. I felt he shouldn't have done it. I was angry and irritable for days. Why did I respond that way? What was I doing? Ah-ha! I was arguing with a done deal.

"Hey, Gramps," I said, "it doesn't make sense to argue with a done deal. What's done is done."

"Right, Dillon!"

"What else can you do in a situation like that?" I asked.

"How about telling yourself, 'It would be nice if he had not put nails in my tires, but he did. So be it.' "

"That makes sense, I guess. You'd feel less stressed. Otherwise it's like trying to swim upstream, against the natural flow of the water."

"Yes, Dillon. This is how people tire so quickly in life. When you argue with a done deal, you are swimming against the current."

We sat in silence for a few moments watching the river flow by. I decided to confide in Grandfather my guilt feelings over my father's death. That was one done deal I couldn't so easily let go.

"He died in my arms, after I had told him to drop dead," I explained. "I didn't mean it. He shouldn't have done that."

56

"Dillon, you are carrying around the painful guilt that his death was your fault. Soon I plan to share with you some techniques which will help you release your anxiety over the drama you had with your father. For now, though, I would like you to trust me and understand that your father truly regrets the abuse you suffered, and you will both benefit when you are able to forgive him. It is a done deal, and it may be time to let go, Dillon."

His words were comforting to me at first. Then I got spooked.

"What??" I gasped. "Hey, Gramps! Are you saying you talk to the dead?"

"No, Dillon, I do not speak with the dead. I call it being sensitive to vibration."

21

SHOTGUN

Grandfather sat down to rest in his rocking chair on the front porch after we had finished our repairs on the roof. I was sitting inside the cabin thinking about my father and feeling depressed again. There was no changing what had happened. I had to put it out of my mind, or I knew I'd go crazy.

I got up and wandered around looking at all the old pictures hanging on the walls. There were a couple of antique shotguns hanging in one corner. I took one down and examined the intricate woodworking someone had done on the stock. All of a sudden the gun blasted and flew out of my hands, knocking me backward, into the wall.

I heard Grandfather yell. The window was blown to bits and the wall around it was completely torn up. Grandfather burst through the cabin door, his eyes bulging and blood gushing from one side of his face. He left a trail of blood on the floor as he crossed the room and grabbed a towel, applying pressure with both hands to the side of his face. His shirt was already stained red. I felt a chill go up my spine and I started to shake. I could have killed him!

"You have crossed the line, Dillon," he said calmly, but I could hear the anger in his voice. "Pack your bags and leave now."

"It was an accident! I was just looking at it!" I yelled. "You're bleeding badly! We need to get you to the hospital!"

"I'll take care of myself. Pack your bags and get out of here, Dillon."

58

"I won't leave you like this! Let me drive you to the hospital, and I'll leave as soon as we get back," I pleaded.

He finally agreed and we left immediately. We rushed down the trail to where his truck was parked on the dirt road. Not a word was spoken during the drive. I worried he may have been weakening from the loss of blood. What if he dies, what if he dies? The words went around and around in my head.

When we arrived at the hospital the doctors took him in right away. I stayed in the emergency room waiting area. I was in a daze. I sat and stared at the wall. I couldn't believe what was happening.

An hour later a doctor came out and told me Sage was lucky he hadn't lost the vision in his right eye. They had done minor surgery to remove the shotgun pellets, and he had required numerous stitches. The doctor said Sage would not tell him how it had happened. I told him it was my fault, but didn't explain anything further. Grandfather did not tell him more, I suspect, because it would mean getting the sheriff involved.

On the way back, Grandfather said he did not think I was mature enough to learn anything more from him, and he questioned whether or not I had learned anything up to this point. He said he was choosing to not invest any more energy in his relationship with me. When we arrived, he wished me well and said good-bye, then went down to the waterfall to meditate.

I grabbed my backpack and left. I wandered into the forest on the connecting national land. I sat down on a rotted-out log and began to weep.

This guy had acted like he really cared, but he didn't give a crap about me. Nobody understands me or what I've been through, I thought. I felt like the biggest loser on earth – a royal jerk and screw-up. Maybe he's right, I thought. Maybe I'm not capable of learning what he's been trying to teach me.

"Is this going to be my whole life?" I cried out. I didn't want to live.

I heard a strong, stern voice then, from deep inside me say, "It is what you choose it to be." Those were Grandfather's words. My inner voice had responded to my question! I had to go back. I could not give up this opportunity. I could learn things from this old man that I knew I couldn't find anywhere else.

I made my way back to Stillpoint. I repeated the words to myself along the way: Life is what you choose it to be. Grandfather was still at the waterfall when I returned.

"I'd like to speak to you, Grandfather. I'm sorry for what I did. I'm asking for your forgiveness and one more chance."

Grandfather opened his eyes and said, "Look, Dillon. You are a guest in my house, and it is your responsibility to honor and respect my space. I feel you have violated my space and that is something I do not tolerate."

"I don't know why I fell into the same hole of stupidity," I said.

"You will continue to step into that hole, Dillon, unless you are able to defuse the pattern behind it."

"What pattern is that?" I asked.

"Your pattern of thinking that says you are a failure and a loser. You attract and create circumstances to support this subconscious pattern."

"Do you mean this shooting incident is a result of my feeling that I'm a screw-up?"

"Of course. You believe it, and you continue to seek confirmation for that which you believe. This allows you to further validate your belief that you are a failure."

"What do I do about it?" I asked.

"First, figure out how you are going to fix my window and the wall. We will deal with your hole later."

I drove into town to get a replacement window, which I paid for with my earnings. Grandfather showed me how to install it. He also taught me about gun safety. He explained that he kept the gun loaded in case of an emergency. He had recently had to kill a rabid raccoon that had come into the yard.

22

EQUALITY

The following morning I was still very upset about the accident with the shotgun. Grandfather sat at the kitchen table repairing the soles on his work boots, as calm as if nothing had ever happened. He sensed my shame and reassured me he would be okay. I couldn't believe he found it so easy to forgive me. In all my life I had never known anyone like him.

I was practicing the hand-warming exercise in an attempt to relax myself when we heard a commotion out in the goat shed. I jumped up and ran to the door to see what was going on.

"Ah," said Grandfather, without even looking up, "it sounds like they are re-establishing their pecking order again."

"You mean they're fighting for dominance over each other?" I asked.

"Right. And the ones who obtain a higher rank in the pecking order feel superior to the ones below. In many species of animals we can see the power struggle of jockeying for position in the herd. It is another part of the survival mechanism we talked about."

"Does this have something to do with why people have such a hard time getting along?" I asked. "Does it have anything to do with me?"

"Yes, Dillon. It has to do with all of us. In its meanest and crudest form, this takes the shape of deep, ugly prejudice and justification for people treating other people as less than human. In its more subtle form, jockeying for position in life can be seen in the arrogance of a person who puts others down or finds fault in others. Control and power games are the means people attempt to use to establish their positions."

"People who assume self-righteous positions are quite easy to identify," Grandfather continued. "It is written all over them when they speak. When one assumes a lower position, that is also easy to read because it shows itself in their insecure body posture."

"Now that I think about it, I guess there have been power struggles going on even among my friends. Like, who gets to be the leader and who ends up following."

"That's right. If you study your life, you will see you have played both roles. By finding fault in others it allows you to feel more secure in your own position. When you are feeling more-than you feel superior, or better, than another person. When you feel less-than you are feeling insecure or inadequate."

"My friends and I sometimes criticize other groups. I guess it makes us feel like we're better than they are."

"That is a delusional way of obtaining security, or sense of position."

"I also remember being in the less-than position," I said. "It seems like some people would like to keep you in that position. They act like they're smarter, or better than you are."

"You will find yourself in a less-than position only if you accept it and allow yourself to feel that way, Dillon. Assuming a less-than position is unnecessary."

"But putting yourself in a more-than position is not good either, right?"

"Right."

"Now I'm confused, Gramps. If you can't put yourself in a more-than position, and it's also wrong to let yourself be in a less-than position, then what position does that leave you?"

"It leaves you," he said, "in a position in which you do not feel the need to judge others. You do not attempt to seek your position in life by comparing yourself to others. And you do not feel you must look up to others as being better than you are. This leaves us all in the position of being equal."

"Equal? I never really thought of it that way," I said. "It sure takes the pressure off."

"I'm not saying we are not to be respectful of others, Dillon. There are people who will serve as your teachers and friends, and they may have more life experience and insight than you do. They may have valuable lessons to share with you. But this does not make them better."

"There are others," he continued, "who may insult you, or violate your space, but still, this does not change the fact that on a deeper level their human life is a gift and is every bit as precious as yours. If we are all created in the image of God, what right do we have to assume anything other than the wisdom to respect and honor the equality and gift of all human life?"

It suddenly became very clear to me how Grandfather was so quickly and easily able to forgive me for all my mistakes; even for the previous day's shooting incident.

23

HEALTHY COMPETITION

Grandfather said he felt like it was a good day to build some new birdhouses, and asked me to go out to the shed and gather together some appropriate pieces of scrap wood while he finished repairing his boots.

He came out a few minutes later and, before I knew it, had constructed two new birdhouses. I was still trying to figure out which pieces of wood I was going to use.

"Slow down, Gramps," I said. "You're way ahead of me."

"This is not a competition, Dillon."

"Hey, I understand about the importance of equality and all that, but what's wrong with a little competition?"

"There is a place for healthy competition, Dillon. But, too often competition becomes another trap."

"Like a weed in the garden of the mind, eh?" I asked, grinning.

"Yes, a weed with deep roots. So, Dillon, you tell me. What do you think healthy competition is?"

"When you play for fun, I guess, and you're not caught up in whether you win or lose."

"Yes, but focus for a minute on what it means if you think you have won or lost."

"People will consider themselves either winners or losers. It's a less-than or more-than situation, right?"

"Yes, if you allow it to be. The key is to understand that losing a game does not make you a loser. There will always be others who perform a particular task above, or below, your performance level on that particular task."

"Like sports, music, mechanical ability, I.Q. tests. . ."

"Yes, all of those things."

"My I.Q. isn't all that high."

"Oh, yeah? Who said so, Dillon?"

"Well, I took the test at school, and. . ."

"Stop right there, Dillon. Who made up the test? God?"

"I guess it was some guy. I don't know who he is."

"Some guy made up a test and someone decided to call it an I.Q. test. Does a high score on that test mean you are intelligent?"

"I think that's what it's supposed to mean, Gramps."

"What it means is, on that particular performance task, you scored a certain way. Who says this guy has a monopoly on the truth regarding what intelligence is? What if we gave him a test based on your life experience? Who would score higher? Dillon, I have known men and women who could not read or write, yet they were great teachers. I know people who would not rank on that I.Q. test, yet they could fix just about anything that was broken, or create magic in their lives. Just because someone scores high on an intelligence test does not mean they are intelligent when it comes to common sense living and getting along with others. It simply means they scored high on that particular performance task."

"I probably would not score very high on that test if I took it right now, Dillon. Would that make me stupid?"

"No, you seem like you've got your act together, Gramps."

"Why, thank you, Dillon," he laughed. "The idea is to have fun in the process of whatever task you are performing. You can feel good if you are pleased by your performance, or disappointed if your performance is not up to par. But this is a passing feeling that does not become a judgement of how you rate yourself in comparison to others. If you are using your performance tasks to judge yourself as to what kind of person you are, then you are caught in the trap."

24

RESPECTING DIFFERENCES

I realized even though I wasn't getting paid much money, Grandfather wasn't working me as hard as I'd expected. We worked only a couple of days a week, and actually spent most of our time outdoors enjoying nature and talking about a lot of things I'd never really given much thought.

After we had hung the new birdhouses we lay on our backs on the hillside above the river, watching huge cirrus clouds pass over. Grandfather pointed out one he thought looked like a Chinese dragon. I thought it looked more like a mermaid.

He asked me if, in the past, I had ever found myself caught up in arguments that left me feeling angry or frustrated.

"Oh, sure. That happens," I replied.

"There is a difference between arguments and disagreements, you know."

"Well, my disagreements often lead to arguments. I've gotten really pissed off at my mother when we try to discuss things. We've had some real blowouts."

"Do you remember those arguments?"

"I remember them like they happened yesterday. I'd get angry because I knew I was right and my mother wouldn't admit she was wrong."

"So, you mean, Dillon, that she was not seeing things the way you think is right, or the way you think she 'should' see things. This is the most common reason for conflict in relationships."

"When you experience friction during a conversation," Grandfather continued, "it is probably because you believe that it is not okay for the other person to disagree with you. You think they are supposed to see the world the way you do."

"So you're saying when I feel an argument brewing, it's because I'm trying to get the other person to see it my way and I'm not willing to let their views be different from mine?"

"That's right, Dillon. And those are the ingredients for a power struggle. You're seeking an 'I am right and you are wrong' solution. People feel justified in their positions, and the truth is things do look different, depending on what perspective you are seeing them from. Accepting differences can lead to greater understanding. By accepting that there are differing views, you become more open to understanding the big picture. It is okay to disagree. How boring the world would be if we were all alike!"

"That makes sense, Gramps. I know a lot of the frustration I've had with people is because they didn't agree with me."

"Acceptance of differences leads to harmony. You can be respectful in your disagreements. It gives people space to be who they are, just as you would like to be given the space to be who you are. How do you feel when someone attempts to take that space away from you?"

"Rebellious."

"And others feel rebellious if you take away their space. So, what will you do, Dillon, if someone becomes irritated with you because they want you to agree with them?"

"I will allow them to be entitled to their viewpoint. I can choose to disagree without arguing."

"Some people will attempt to get you to fight back

by pushing your buttons, Dillon. They can tell when they push a button in you."

"How?"

"It shows on your face and it is easy to read. Once they see you react, they will go after the buttons even stronger in an attempt to get you off base. People do not like a one-way argument because it makes them feel foolish, so they will work hard at drawing you into it."

"I have to focus on not getting pulled in."

"Yes, and you can also suggest discussing the matter at another time, when emotions are not so flared. The key, Dillon, is to stay firm in your conviction that it is okay for people to be different and they do not have to conform to how you think they should think and act. People will notice this and appreciate your acceptance of their differences. It is a sign of maturity and shows others you are aware of your boundaries."

"I'm not sure I know what you mean by boundaries."

"There is a dance of energy that takes place in relationships, Dillon. Boundaries are the quality of interpersonal space we create with a person or circumstance at any given moment."

"They are not fixed boundaries then," I said.

"No, they change from moment to moment based on the type and quality of interaction we are having. There are two extremes of unhealthy boundaries: enmeshed boundaries and disengaged boundaries. In the middle of the two extremes is where one establishes healthy boundaries. You will find yourself being pulled toward enmeshment or disengagement in relationships. The key is to monitor your own energy."

"How can you be sure which way you are being pulled?"

"Dillon, have you ever had a phone call, and as soon as you heard the person's voice you felt a knot forming in your gut?"

"Sure. There are a few people who make me feel that way."

"What?! Make you feel that way? Are you telling me you are a victim and people toss your feelings around like a horseshoe?"

"Okay. I guess I should say I allow my buttons to get pushed."

"Yes, this is one type of enmeshment. Your field becomes entangled with another's and you lose your sense of personal identity. But no one has the right to violate your space. Even if people attempt to trespass in your space, you do not have to let them in. Every person is responsible for living their own life and bearing the consequences of their behavior. Have compassion and care for others, but do not lose your space in their space."

"Then disengaged boundaries must be the opposite. You disconnect from the situation."

"Yes. While enmeshment is like a hot type of response, disengagement is a cold response."

"I think I've done that. It's like I shut myself off from the world or another person. One day my boundaries with my mother were enmeshed. Every little thing she did or said pissed me off. The next day I disengaged, and when she spoke to me, I nodded and said 'uh huh,' but I didn't hear a word she said."

"Why do you think people develop disengaged boundaries, Dillon?"

"Probably because they feel overloaded or hurt, and disconnecting is their defense."

"Right. And people who adopt this as a relationship style can feel isolated and lonely. When our boundaries are healthy, we are neither disconnected nor overwhelmed. If you find yourself moving toward the disengaged pole, you can re-engage a little so that your colder energy warms up some. Compassion is neither hot nor cold. It is a balanced warm energy."

"When our boundaries are healthy," Grandfather continued, "we are respectful of other people's space. We do not view them as less-than or more-than we are, regardless of their behavior. We do not get overdrawn into their drama, but we do not disconnect either."

"I know now how I've been creating friction in my relationships," I said. "I'll have to work at recognizing boundaries, though."

"You have come a long way already, just by being aware of this, Dillon."

"Accepting differences would help maintain equality," I said. "No one is better-than or less-than."

"I could not have said it better myself, Dillon."

25

THE MAGIC WITHIN

We went for a long walk early one morning and stopped in a field full of colorful wildflowers and surrounded by dense forest. In the center of the field was a huge oak tree. We leaned against the trunk and looked out across the field.

I saw a hummingbird darting about among the wildflowers, then stopping in mid-air, its wings just a blur. I saw a spider spinning a web and was amazed at the complex geometric pattern. A squirrel balanced on a small limb. A butterfly gracefully landed on a wildflower.

"Dillon, can you feel that the trees reach to the sun and the sun reaches to the trees? The clouds have a relationship with the wind, just as the birds have a relationship with the sky. Do you see a common denominator?"

"The common denominator I see is a natural intelligence."

"What do you mean by intelligence, Dillon?"

"Well, how could a little bird fly south across oceans and mountain ranges and back again to the same nest unless nature was intelligent?"

"I've wondered the same thing. Instinct is God's intelligence working through all forms of nature. The earth and other planets in our solar system know their paths around the sun. Can you feel the magic of it all?"

"I can see it, but I'm not sure how much I feel it."

"Guess what, Dillon? You are part of that magic. That magic moves in you. It moves in your blood and it dances in your soul. You are not separate or isolated from God's intelligence. You are connected to it. How is it your hair knows to grow back the same color? How is it your fingernails grow back when you cut them? The intelligence you see in the beauty of nature expresses itself through you as well. But, do you know what it is that makes you unique in comparison to nature?"

"No, I don't."

"What will that sparrow be tomorrow, Dillon?"

"A sparrow."

"And what will that sparrow be next year?"

"A sparrow."

"How about ten years from now?"

"It'll probably be dead, Gramps."

"That's right, Dillon. Could it have changed its mind and been something other than a sparrow?"

"No. Once it's born a sparrow, it lives and dies a sparrow."

"Dillon, how are you different from that sparrow?"

"I have more choices?" I guessed.

"Yes, you have choices. You can learn and grow, and become more than you have been. You can develop your insight in ways you have yet to imagine. You can choose to embrace your life as an exciting journey, or you can take it for granted and sleep through the ride. Your ability to choose is what creates your uniqueness and guides your experience. Value the gift of choice, for it is the treasure that leads to your destiny."

We picked some wildflowers to take back to the cabin. I put them in a vase on the kitchen table. After lunch Grandfather handed me a small box with a ribbon on it. He said it was to express his appreciation for the work I had done. I opened the box and stared, in shock, at what I saw inside. It was the arrowhead from his collection that I had taken and then returned.

"I thought it would make a nice necklace, Dillon," he said, looking intently into my eyes.

I was speechless. He fixed a black cord to the arrowhead and I put it around my neck. Tears beaded up in my eyes. How do these coincidences keep happening? I wondered. I thought about what he had told me under the oak tree in the field of wildflowers: Value the gift of choice, for it is the treasure that leads to your destiny.

I always have choices. The holes I keep falling in are a result of my faulty choices. I was glad I had chosen to put the arrowhead back.

26

KNOWING WHEN YOU ARE OUT OF TUNE

Later that afternoon Grandfather said he was
going across the river to check on a stand of bamboo he
had planted last year. I asked if I could join him. We had
to cross the river by walking across a fallen tree resting
several feet above the water. Grandfather skipped across,
while I cautiously inched along a half step at a time.

Grandfather was pleased to find the bamboo had
nearly doubled in size. He offered to show me how to
make a bamboo flute. He looked over each stalk before
choosing one, and then gave thanks to the bamboo before
he cut it.

We sat down while he carved and filed the bamboo
to create a flute. When he had finished he played a few
scales, and then surprised me by bursting into a very
rhythmic and high-spirited melody. I applauded him
afterward. Then he played another song that was obviously
out of tune.

"What did you think of that song, Dillon?" he
asked.

"To be honest with you, I didn't like it as well as the
first one because it sounded out of tune."

"How did you know?"

"Well, I just knew, I guess."

"What do you mean, you just knew?"

"I don't know. I just knew."

"Dillon, I think you were able to observe that my
second song was out of tune and out of rhythm because
you have a reference point."

"What do you mean?"

"You compared it in your mind to what you think an 'in tune' song sounds like. The 'in tune' song is your reference point." Grandfather handed the flute to me. I tried playing a few notes.

"I guess people can be in tune or out of tune, too, eh?" I said.

"That's true, Dillon. What do you think it means to be in tune?"

I immediately thought back to our conversations about being centered in balance and harmony, and how, if we have clouds in our mind, they block our inner sunlight.

"Being out of tune means you are off center, right? Like getting caught up in your own drama or someone else's soap opera. You feel agitated or frustrated."

"Yes. It is like being in the soup and not even knowing you are being cooked! Each of us has the potential to get out of the soup, Dillon, but unfortunately many people do not even know when they are in it."

"Are you talking about me?" I asked.

"It is your personal responsibility to figure that out, Dillon. If a person has not developed a strong reference point of being calm, centered and harmonious, they may not recognize when they are out of tune."

"It seems like sometimes I have no control over myself. I've probably been a real jerk and didn't even know it."

"I have had my share of putting my foot in my mouth, too, Dillon. The point is, it is crucial that we develop an internal reference point."

"How do you do that?"

"You practice being in tune. You form a memory of what it feels like to be balanced and, in all your activities, you operate from that space."

"And, just as important," Grandfather continued, "you practice recognizing when you are out of tune. Without this commitment, you cannot learn to live a life of harmony."

"It seems to me, Gramps, you're saying that learning to recognize when we are out of tune can help us in observing the effects of our own behavior."

"Yes, it can, Dillon, if we are willing."

27

ANOTHER HOLE

Although I had been at Stillpoint for only a few weeks, those weeks felt like months. On one hand it seemed like so much had happened my head was spinning, yet, on the other hand, absolutely nothing was going on.

I enjoyed the peacefulness and the beauty of the mountains, but often found myself wondering what I was missing out on back at home, in the real world. A war could have broken out and we wouldn't have known about it. Grandfather had a radio, but seldom turned it on.

We had worked for three days building a new shed that was now finished. I thought it was a good time to ask if I could take a little break. It was late afternoon on a Saturday and I was feeling especially restless.

"Hey, Gramps," I said, "if it's okay with you, I thought I'd go home tonight and come back in a few days."

"Sounds like something is cooking, Dillon. Anything you would like to talk about?"

"Oh, I don't know. I just feel like a need a break. I want to see my friends."

"Your leaving is not what concerns me. I feel you are running away from yourself."

"What do you mean, Gramps?" I started feeling impatient.

"You came here this summer to work, and I do not think you expected to be going through these changes in your life. You have learned a lot in a short period of time and that can be scary. Your old world has been shaken up."

"I'm not scared. I just want to get out of here for a

few days."

"You are not the same young man who came here. Your model of reality is in the process of change. I wonder if letting go of your old self is a challenge for you."

"I'm getting tired of all this philosophical stuff, Gramps. Living with you is intense. I just need a break. Will you let me go?"

"Of course, Dillon. This is not a prison. And if you decide you would rather not come back, that's your choice."

"I'll be back," I smiled, feeling relieved. "I want to come back. I kind of like it out here."

I took my backpack and walked down the trail and followed the dirt road out to the main highway to hitch a ride. Within just a few minutes a car stopped. As I approached the car I saw three guys about my age inside, all drinking beer. The voice of life flashed a big red flag before my eyes: "Do not get in the car." I thought maybe I was just being paranoid. They seemed friendly, just out having fun and getting a little rowdy. I really didn't feel like waiting for another ride. One of them swung open the back door and I climbed in.

I noticed a number of empty beer cans on the floor. One of the guys offered me a beer. I started to refuse it, but changed my mind. I was actually quite thirsty from the walk. It tasted great. We were cruising down the road with the stereo turned up and everyone singing along. I started feeling like my old self again.

We hadn't gone very far when we passed by a highway patrol car parked by the side of the road, partially concealed by shrubs. I glanced at the speedometer. We were speeding. The guy who was driving saw the worried look on my face. He laughed and sped up even more. Evidently no one else had seen the patrol car.

"Hey, man, there's a cop!" I shouted to be heard over the blaring music. It was too late. The police were already coming up behind us.

"Aw, shit! Not again," the driver moaned and shut the music off. "Hey, I was just goofing around with you," he said to me. The other two guys were trying frantically to shove all the empty beer cans under the seats.

The patrol car's flashing lights came on and we pulled onto the shoulder of the road and stopped. The guys were all cussing about their bad luck. I felt numb. All I had wanted was to go home for a few days.

When the officers began to ask questions, the driver, trying to be funny, responded with some sarcastic remarks, and that was the end of my trip home. We were all handcuffed and taken to the local jail. I explained my situation to the police. I told them how to get in touch with Grandfather Sage and that he would come and get me.

A few hours later Grandfather showed up. He was brought to our cell and when he was asked if he knew any of us, he looked at me and said, "Never seen any of them before." He turned and walked out.

I was furious. The rest of the guys were already passed out, but I didn't sleep a wink all night.

In the morning Grandfather returned. He told the officer he thought he had made a mistake and perhaps he did recognize one of the young men. He spoke with the police chief in private. I was released.

"Why did you make me spend the night in jail?" I demanded. "I can't believe you would do that to me! Did you get a kick out of it? I'm pissed at you!"

He made no apologies. He didn't even respond to my accusations. He was as cheerful as if nothing had happened. He stopped the truck at a small market and said, "I will be right back." He returned a few minutes later with a large bag of popcorn.

"For the theater of life, Dillon," he grinned. We ate the popcorn on the way back to the cabin.

28

THE TRANCES OF EVERYDAY LIFE

That afternoon back at the cabin Grandfather was shucking corn he'd had left over from the previous year's harvest that he intended to cut from the cobs and feed to the squirrels. I sat at the kitchen table watching him, too exhausted to do anything. I was depressed. I felt foolish for having gotten myself into another jam. I hadn't even made it to the next county without getting into trouble.

"Do not wallow in your guilt, Dillon. Just figure out what really happened and move on."

"Before I got in the car with those guys a big red flag went up, but I ignored it."

"Sounds to me like you sabotaged yourself again. Those messages you picked up from your environment and your father have become your core beliefs."

"But my father is dead. He can't put me down anymore."

"Your father treated you like you were not good enough."

"Yeah. Whatever I did, it wasn't good enough."

"Those messages still exist in your subconscious and affect your present experience. Dillon, he was just mirroring to you his own inadequacy. Your father is no longer physically present, but his messages live on in the form of your underlying belief that you will never amount to anything." Grandfather set aside the corn he was shucking and sat down across from me at the kitchen table.

"Isn't it interesting that you keep finding yourself in situations which confirm this?" he asked.

"It does seem to keep happening. I just wind up in the wrong place at the wrong time."

"Don't you get it, Dillon? You do not just end up there by accident. Your underlying beliefs generate an actual vibration that is constantly emanating from you. A part of you attracts these circumstances and allows you to engage in the drama."

"Some people cannot handle it when things are going smoothly," he continued. "They look for arguments, or create a crisis. Then a part of them can say, 'Yeah, this is more like it. Now it feels normal.' They may not be aware they are being governed this way, but they are. They grew up in crisis, and as an adult they seek out crisis because that is what feels normal to them."

I suddenly realized what he had been trying to tell me all along. I shook my head and let out a sigh. It made sense.

"Life is a process, Dillon, in which we learn to wake up from the trances of everyday life. Emotional trances interfere with our ability to live in harmony."

"You've said harmony is our true nature."

"Yes, Dillon. And emotional patterns that take us out of balance are reflections of these trances."

"Are you saying it's not good to feel?" I asked.

"I am saying there is a difference between emotions and feelings. Many emotions are patterns recreating themselves without your permission. They are stuck, or unfinished, parts of yourself which resurface as they are triggered. They exaggerate and color your responses."

"Feelings, on the other hand, are spontaneous and appropriate reactions to the moment. Your dog dies and you feel sad. Your sadness was not a recreation of an unresolved part of yourself. But if you overreact to spilled milk, then your anger is an emotional trance. Many people live their lives moving from one emotional trance into another. One moment they might feel insecure. The next moment they may be judgmental. Another moment they may be embellishing their sense of superiority."

"How can you wake up from the trance when you don't even know you're in it?" I asked.

"That is a process which develops over time. First, we learn to recognize the trances of our everyday life. Then we play detective and get to observe ourselves involved in these trances. Then we learn to wake up. Have fun with your new insights. Don't be too hard on yourself when you catch yourself off center. Being hard on yourself is another type of trance."

"I know that one," I said.

"Have the courage to examine yourself. You can have fun discovering who you are *not*, and then you can discover who you *are*. These trances are not who you really are."

"Then who am I?"

"Remove your programming and you will find out."

29

SNAKES AND COLORED LENSES

After splitting and stacking some firewood after dinner that night I collapsed under a tree to relax for a while before going to bed. Grandfather came out of the cabin and lay down on the grass.

"By the way, Dillon, I forgot to tell you there are rattlesnakes and copperheads in these woods. Be careful."

"I don't like snakes. Have you ever been bitten, Gramps?"

"Only a few times. I almost died once, but I guess it was not my time to go." He smiled and I wasn't sure whether he was telling the truth or not.

He got up and went back into the cabin and returned a few minutes later with a basket of fruit. I was about to bite into an apple when suddenly Grandfather's eyes opened wide and he shouted, "Look out!" He reached to my side and picked up a two-foot long snake and began wrestling with it.

I sprang to my feet and ran thirty feet across the yard before I looked back. I saw Grandfather rolling on the ground, laughing. Then I realized what I had thought was a snake was a piece of rubber hose he'd brought from the cabin concealed among the fruit.

"That was mean, Gramps," I said. "Why did you yell 'look out for that snake?' "

"I didn't, Dillon. I simply said 'look out.' Your mind created the rest of the story. You saw what you feared. Your fear was projected into the world and that piece of garden hose became your fear."

"But it looked real. I could have sworn that hose was a snake."

"Dillon, when I was a youth I was very self-conscious. One day a group of people were staring at me. I was convinced they were talking about me until I realized they were actually looking at someone standing behind me."

"You know, Gramps, the same thing happened to me once. I was in a large stadium watching a football game. When one of the teams went into a huddle, I just knew they were talking about me."

"Are you serious, Dillon?"

"I got you, Gramps."

He smiled. "Well, I am glad to hear you are kidding."

"I know what you're talking about, though," I said. "What you believe inside affects what you perceive on the outside. If you're gloomy inside, life can look gloomy on a sunny day."

"Yes, and if you are bright on the inside, life will feel and look bright even on a gloomy day."

"I once had a pair of glasses that had a blue tint to them. I wore them all day. After a while I forgot I was wearing them and wondered why everything looked so bluish. Later, when I took the lenses off everything looked very different."

"So what's the moral of your story, Dillon?"

"We don't always see as clearly as we think we're seeing. We think we're seeing and experiencing the world as it is, but in reality we're only seeing the world as it's reflected through our colored lenses."

"Yes, Dillon. These lenses can be made up of many different colors, thicknesses and textures, which are the unresolved wounds we carry around with us – hurts, rejections, fears and resentments that have not healed.

Limiting beliefs and conditioning color our perceptions. Many people go through an entire lifetime without questioning, and with little change in how they view reality."

"My experience with that hose was one of those colored lenses," I said.

"It sure was, Dillon," Grandfather chuckled.

"I went into a full-blown survival mechanism fight/flight response."

"Isn't it wonderful that you got to confront your fear face to face, Dillon?"

"Very funny, Gramps."

30

BREATHING AND THE MIND

Grandfather loved to study animals. He would get as close as he could without being noticed, and observe them as they lived their lives. I was unaware of it, but one morning he was tracking me.

I was sitting on the river bank basking in the sun and feeling very relaxed. He managed to creep up to within a foot behind me without my knowing. He let out a vicious growl that sounded just like a bear. I nearly jumped out of my skin.

"Gramps," I said, when I had regained my composure, "you seem to find great enjoyment in doing these kinds of things to me."

"I do, Dillon."

"How come I'm not able to sneak up on you like that?"

He laughed. "That is for you to figure out. Did you happen to notice how your breathing pattern changed when you were startled?"

"I gasped. I breathed in with my upper chest."

"Right. When you feel threatened or startled you breathe with your middle and upper chest. Abdominal, or diaphragmatic, breathing is the way nature intended us to breathe."

"How do you know that, Gramps?"

"Did you ever watch a baby's breathing?"

"Oh, yeah. I remember watching his belly go up and down as he breathed."

"Just as a baby naturally knows how to suck on the

breast, she also knows how to breathe. Babies have just come from the heavenly realms and have not lost their rhythm."

"Why don't we continue to breathe like that as we grow up?"

"We do until we learn otherwise. Many people adopt middle and upper chest breathing patterns because they do not feel safe and secure. Your breathing pattern is like a mirror of your mind. If you are not feeling safe, it will be reflected in your breathing and you will breathe in your middle and upper chest."

"Like I did when you sneaked up on me, and like I did when I thought I saw that snake."

"Yes, Dillon. When a baby feels his needs are not being met, he breathes hysterically. If you watch someone who is in a panic, you see them gasping with a total restriction on their exhalation."

"I remember getting that way as a kid, when I was really upset. I breathed in and in, but had trouble breathing out. It seems if we are breathing in our middle or upper chest, it means we are out of tune."

"Exactly, Dillon. And since breathing mirrors your feelings, changing your breathing pattern will change how you feel. If you are feeling stressed and uptight and you begin to breathe the way a relaxed person breathes, your state of mind will change. The uptight feelings will dissolve."

"So all I have to do to overcome feelings of stress is to breathe in my belly?" I asked.

"Yes, and allow your belly to go soft when you breathe out. When your belly goes soft it means there is minimal restriction during your exhalation."

"That's like breathing a sigh of relief, isn't it? You're feeling safe and secure and like everything is okay.

You breathe out with no restrictions."

"Right, Dillon, and that is because your breathing pattern is mirroring your mind at that time. What would happen if, in the next moment, you were not aware and began thinking about your problems or worries?"

"My breathing pattern would shift to middle and upper chest breathing because I would no longer feel safe."

"Your task, Dillon, is to learn to apply this to your everyday life. You will see your breathing pattern as a friend that reveals to you your state of mind. It will assist you with understanding yourself."

31

BEING VS. THINKING

That evening we took sleeping bags and hiked to the top of the highest ridge in the area. It was the day of summer solstice and Grandfather wanted to celebrate by spending the night under the stars. There was a magnificent view of the foothills all around us. The sun was setting. We sat on a rock outcropping facing west and watched the changing colors in the sky and the colorful cloud formations passing over.

"Did you ever sit on a bench and watch people go by?" Grandfather asked.

"Yes, I have," I replied. "It seemed like everyone was in a world of their own, as if they were living their own personal soap operas. I could see it on their faces as they walked by."

"I have some interesting news for you, Dillon. You are living your own soap opera, too. If we took a video of your mind from the time you woke up until the time you went to sleep, what would we find?"

"We'd probably find that I waste a lot of time."

"Waste time on what?"

"Trivial things, I guess, that really don't matter. I'm always doing, or going, or thinking."

"Where do those mental activities take you, Dillon?"

"Into either the past or the future, I guess."

"Yes. The mind gets caught up in lots of thoughts, and there is a lack of awareness where much personal drama gets created. The mind often runs on automatic pilot. Thoughts come and go without your permission."

"That happens to me all the time. I'll tell myself I don't want to think about something anymore, but it keeps coming back to me."

"Do you give it permission to come back?"

"No."

"Then those thought patterns are on automatic pilot. Those thoughts are thinking you. Awareness is when you choose to think your thoughts. You are aware that you are thinking. It's like driving a stick shift. You can choose to shift into past thought, or you can shift into future thought in order to plan your schedule. But you also have the freedom to choose to shift out of thinking."

"How can you shift out of thinking? If you're not thinking, what are you doing?" I asked.

"I know you understand, Dillon, because you have been there before. Where have you been when you have not been thinking?"

"I don't know, Gramps."

"Quiet your mind and you will remember."

My mind became restless as I tried to force it to be still.

"Dillon, you are swimming upstream. Go with the flow. You cannot force your mind to be still. You allow your mind to enter into stillness."

I stopped trying to force my thoughts to leave and allowed them to be like the clouds floating across the sky. After a while the clouds thinned out and the thoughts diminished. I felt a stillness and deep sense of peace.

"Now you are learning to connect with your true nature, Dillon. The nature of pure being."

I wasn't thinking. I wasn't caught up in thoughts of where I was supposed to be going, or what I was supposed to be doing next. I was simply being.

"There is a place for thinking, Dillon, but if you get

too caught up in it, that is when you get lost in your soap opera. 'Being' is about awakening into the awareness of the present moment. Awareness is the key to embracing the present. When you walk, you are aware you are walking. When you think, you are aware you are thinking."

"And as I am listening to your words," I said, "I'm aware that I am listening. When I speak to you, I'm aware that I am speaking. I'm feeling aware of each moment."

"Isn't it nice to just hang out with yourself?" Grandfather asked. "There is nowhere you have to go and nothing you must become, nothing you have to do and nothing you have to say. Just hang out and be present to your experience."

"It feels wonderful to just be," I said.

I could hear a high-pitched ringing, similar to the sound of crickets. Grandfather explained this universal sound has no beginning, middle or end. The world is always changing, but the sound remains. It is a constant throughout all time. When we connect with this sound we are in unity with the vibratory sound current which rings throughout the universe. He calls it "God's flute." He listens to it all the time, even while he is hearing the other sounds in the environment.

32

BREATHING AND BEING

I gathered some sticks and we built a small camp-fire when the last light of dusk had gone.

"Dillon, I am going to hang out with myself and you are welcome to join me." Grandfather meant he was choosing to no longer talk and was entering into the stillness of silence. He was letting go of thinking and moving into being fully present to the moment. That's what he referred to as "hanging out."

Once again it took me some time to clear my thoughts. I gazed up at the stars for awhile. My thoughts eventually slowed down and I let them go as if they were birds flying across the sky.

At last I entered into the wonderful stillness of being, that harmonious feeling of being present and complete, the total acceptance of being in the moment in that place beyond words. Time seemed to stand still. We hung out until the fire died down and just a few coals remained. The full moon was beginning to rise.

"Dillon, I enjoyed sharing that sacred space with you. It is a way in which we communicate deeply without words. Now I would like to communicate with words."

"What would you like to talk about?" I asked.

"What did you notice, Dillon, when you were fully present in the moment?"

"When I was in the stillness of being I had no thoughts."

"It is in the pause between your thoughts that you experience the awareness of being. The only way to

95

experience the moment, Dillon, is to leave past or future preoccupations behind. The fullness of the moment can be experienced only from the center of your being. The awareness of your being lives in the pause between your thoughts."

"It seemed like when I was in the deepest experience of being, my breathing slowed down, and almost stopped," I said.

"When you are in the pause between thoughts you can simultaneously experience the pause between your breaths. Following your exhalation there is a pause, and then you breathe in again. As you merge into the joy of being, that pause lengthens. For spiritual growth it is important to develop a relationship with the pause between your thoughts because this is where you experience the radiance of your soul."

"That is why," Grandfather continued, "you breathe only about five to ten breaths a minute in the communion of being. What a deeply peaceful and harmonious feeling that is," he paused for a moment. "But if you are thinking without awareness, you are typically breathing twelve to eighteen breaths a minute."

"So that means more of your time is spent inhaling and exhaling, instead of in the pause of being that occurs between breaths," I said.

"Yes, Dillon. Unfortunately many people miss the splendor of the moment. They end up riding the merry-go-round of thoughts. From the time they wake up until the time they go to sleep, the thoughts go around and around."

"I know how tiring that can be," I said. "You can become quite dizzy and off balance if you don't know how to step off the merry-go-round."

33

I AM THE WITNESS OF MY SHOW

Grandfather went into town one morning to get some building materials. I stayed behind. I had been eyeing a huge old oak tree in the yard that had a strong branch up high, perfect for hanging a swing. I decided to put it up and surprise Grandfather when he returned.

I found everything I needed in the shed and climbed up the tree to fasten the ropes. I sanded a scrap of pinewood I'd found for the seat and applied a dark stain that brought out the beauty of the wood grain.

I had gone down to the river for a swim when Grandfather returned a couple of hours later. When I got back I found him swinging, and singing one of his happy nature songs. I sat down and listened.

He was very pleased with the swing and complimented me on my craftsmanship. He asked me to take off my arrowhead necklace for a moment. I handed it to him and he began swinging it back and forth like a pendulum. He let the pendulum come to a rest and explained that this represents the stillpoint, or the center, where our soul shines through without obstruction.

When the pendulum swings, it swings away from the center. It may swing into the caution zone, or even further, into the danger zone. Our safe zone is the range in which our pendulum swings from left to right while we are able to remain calm and aware.

"What's the caution zone?" I asked.

"That is where you get so off center you begin to feel or act imbalanced. Know what I mean?"

"Well," I said, "my old tendency was to act cool even though I was feeling insecure. I worried about things I couldn't change. I'd get irritable when things didn't go the way I thought they should."

"Yes, Dillon. Those are examples of the caution zone, maybe even the danger zone. In the caution zone the trance, or fog, is not as thick. You are able to step back and observe that you are no longer in the safe zone. You can then choose to return to the safe zone. It's like stepping out of a trance. It is a lot easier to catch yourself off track and return to the safe zone when you are in the caution zone."

"Because you're not so far off from center?"

"Exactly. When you move way off center it takes a lot more energy to get yourself out of that denser trance. This is why awareness is important. Awareness allows us to monitor the pendulum swing."

"I guess if you lack awareness you fall into the hole again. Same old game, and same old trance."

"Yes, Dillon. Our job is to learn how to function in the safe zone. Practice will allow you to notice when you are in the caution or danger zones. You will learn to bring yourself back into the balance of the safe zone."

"Is that all there is to it?" I asked.

"Why complicate something that is so simple? At any given moment you can step into awareness. You become a witness. Guess what you are witnessing."

"I guess I'm witnessing whatever's going on with me."

"Exactly. If you are being insecure, you get to witness your insecurity. If you are being self-centered, you get to observe that. If you are worrying, you see you are worrying. If your mind is racing, you see you are ahead of yourself. You witness whatever trance you may be in."

"It's like observing myself in my own movie theater."

"Yes, Dillon. And guess what?" he laughed. "You have the best seat in the house! If you see yourself acting like you are better than someone else, you get to observe your judgmental attitude. You discover that you are in a trance of superiority. If you are acting or feeling like you are not good enough, you get to witness your feelings of inadequacy. The good news, Dillon, is when you are observing yourself, when you are the witness, you are in the safe zone."

"You mean when I am observing I'm living in the safe zone?" I asked.

"Of course. That is because you, the observer, and awareness are one and the same."

"That's amazing, Gramps! All I have to do is be the observer and I'm in the safe zone."

"That's all there is to it, Dillon. When you are aware, you are mindful of wherever you are and whatever it is you are doing."

"Then being the observer teaches us to recognize our trances," I said.

"Yes, it does. At any given moment all you have to do is ask, 'What am I doing, thinking or feeling at this moment?' Just keep being the observer," he said. "Be the witness and be aware of what you are witnessing. Then you wake up."

"You mean I wake up from the trance of in-adequacy or superiority or greed or worry?"

"Yes. You snap out of it because you have now become the observer of the drama, rather than the victim."

"What do you mean by victim?"

"Before you became aware, Dillon, those patterns were occurring without your permission."

"This all makes so much sense, Gramps. Why don't they teach us this in school?"

"Maybe someday students will be able to study these concepts as part of a personal growth curriculum. Let's just say you are learning them in the planetary schoolhouse, the great classroom of life!"

34

TURNING POINT

One afternoon I was getting ready to spread some mulch in the garden when Grandfather came out and told me he thought it would be a good idea to give my mother a call to see how she was doing. I told him I would call her that evening. He insisted I call right away. I went down to the general store to use the telephone.

My aunt answered the phone. She was packing a bag of clothes to take to my mother, who was in the hospital. Earlier in the day a bicyclist had run into Mom as she was crossing the street, knocking her over backward. She had suffered a broken leg and hit her head on the concrete.

Grandfather said I could borrow his truck. I packed a few things and left immediately. Mom was released from the hospital the next day and was able to get around somewhat with crutches.

For two days I helped Mom with food preparation and chores. My aunt, who lived nearby, was able to help as well, so Mom insisted I return to Stillpoint and finish my summer work with Grandfather Sage. She was concerned that if stayed I would get caught up in an old rut with my friends. I agreed, and planned to leave early the following day.

Later, while I was doing some grocery shopping for Mom, I ran into one of my friends. When I returned home, four other guys called, insisting we go out and party that night. I decided to go.

I met them at the park where we used to hang out.

They brought a couple cases of beer and began the old routine. I sipped on one beer for the next two hours while some of the other guys drank more than a six-pack each. I felt like I was watching a movie. I observed very curiously how my group of friends interacted. I could see how they were caught up in judging and putting others down and how this gave them a false sense of superiority. They were bragging and seeking to secure a more-than position. I saw how some of them were doing this in response to feeling in an insecure, less-than position.

I chose not to be drawn into the game. I shared my observations about how we often strive to secure our positions in the herd. I explained that we don't have to play that game, and it is more peaceful to assume a position of equality which respects differences and honors the idea that we have all been created in the image of God.

At first they thought I was joking, but soon realized I meant what I said. They became defensive when they realized I would not engage in the old judgment game we used to play. Frank, who is most into the trance of control and power, got angry and called me a jerk. The king rooster thought I was jockeying for his position! I knew they couldn't understand where I was coming from, so I let it go.

The conversation moved to a number of superficial topics that seemed shallow to me. I couldn't believe that not long ago I had hung out with these guys on a daily basis and this was how I had thought and acted. Focusing on sex, money and partying no longer had the same appeal. I sat in silence.

Frank confronted me again. "What's wrong with you, man?" he demanded. "Have you sold out on us? What has that old guy you're working for done to you? Have you been brainwashed, or what?"

I replied that I felt I used to live my life surrounded by a thick fog, and now I was beginning to awaken from the trance. They had no idea what I was talking about. I attempted to explain how we are walking around with colored lenses that color the way we see the world. I explained how our self-talk affects us. We can learn to observe our own soap opera, I told them, and awareness is a tool which brings us to a deeper understanding of ourselves. They looked at each other, dumbfounded.

I explained there is a difference between thoughts that habitually think us, and choosing to think our thoughts. We can develop a relationship with the space between our thoughts, I explained, and experience the pureness of being, which lives in present awareness. They shook their heads and looked at me like I was crazy.

Then Frank said, "Let's go get some more beer and pick up some girls." They jumped in Joe's van and wanted me to come along. I was sure Joe was intoxicated, and I refused. I chose to go home instead.

I stared up at the ceiling as I lay in bed. I felt trapped between two worlds. I no longer fit into my old world with my friends. They didn't understand me, and I wasn't sure I really understood Grandfather's world. It seemed as if I had come to a fork in the road, torn between two paths. One path was my old world; the other path, Grandfather's world.

I imagined my future on the old path. It grew darker and darker over time. I pictured myself taking Grandfather's road. The path got brighter as time moved forward. Grandfather's road led to freedom. There was no turning back.

I remembered the vision I'd had prior to meeting Grandfather. I had really seen his face, but dismissed it as a figment of my imagination. I was suddenly overwhelmed with a strong feeling from deep inside. Ah-ha! The magic of the universe had arranged our meeting! My relationship with Grandfather was the greatest gift I had ever received. I couldn't wait to get back to Stillpoint.

35

THE MAIN ROAD

When I arrived at Stillpoint early the next afternoon I found Grandfather meditating down by the waterfall. I tried to sneak up behind him. I got within ten feet of him and he turned around and smiled.

"Did you get lost, Dillon?"

"No, I didn't," I said. "It was an easy drive."

"That's good. I knew there was a fork in the road and I am glad you chose the right path." His response took me by surprise.

"Gramps, I don't know how you happen to know these things. I do know you're not as weird as I used to think you were."

"Why, thank you, Dillon. You are not quite as weird as you used to seem to me, as well. Anyway, the fun has just begun."

"What do you mean by that?"

"Now that you have consciously chosen which path you are taking, you will be able to assimilate a new level of experience."

I didn't understand until many weeks later what he meant.

That evening Grandfather gathered sticks from the forested area surrounding Stillpoint and built a special campfire to welcome me back. I told him about my trip home and what I had observed among my friends. He sat smiling and listening, but didn't say a word. I eventually finished my story and allowed my mind to clear of thoughts. Nearly an hour passed before Grandfather broke the silence.

"Dillon, you are going through a wonderful growth process, and these adventures are preparing you for the next stage in this process. You have made some very positive changes in the quality of your thought. You will begin to attract friends who will nourish you, and likewise, you will nourish them. You have become more aware of the synchronicities of life. You know the universe is on your side and working in your best interest."

"Synchronicities?" I asked.

"That means life's events are not occurring merely by chance."

"I'm beginning to feel like life does have an arrangement."

"Yes, an amazing arrangement that perplexes the mind as we experience the interconnecting web of life. I have no doubts about it. I have seen the evidence of it over and over again. The universe provides in mysterious ways. Sometimes we are aware of it, and other times we are not."

"I think you and me getting together was synchronicity," I said.

"Yes, Dillon. This is cosmic arrangement. It was not chance that our paths have crossed. We are connected to the whole of life, and life is responding by providing us the lessons we are ready to receive. Life experience is a great teacher."

"It's amazing, Gramps! Life is intelligent and the universe holds it all together through synchronicity."

"As you are in the process of developing yourself, Dillon, you will attract, and be attracted to, friends who will resonate with you."

"You mean we'll be on the same wavelength?" I asked.

"Yes. Birds of a feather flock together."

"I've changed so much that, instead of being attracted to the guys I used to hang out with, I felt repelled. I'm on a different wavelength now."

"You are. Your brainwave patterns are different than they were before. A shift has taken place within you, and now you will attract and seek friends who are on a parallel wavelength. To spend your time with those who are not committed to personal growth may feel stagnating to you."

"It's no fun to hang around people who keep falling in the same old holes, especially if they're not interested in getting out of the hole," I said.

"Dillon, do not get cocky. You still have your share of holes."

"Back off, Gramps. I'm not copping a better-than attitude."

"Just checking, Dillon." I thought I saw him smile in the flickering light of the fire. We sat quietly for a few moments.

"So, Dillon, if you saw a friend falling in the same hole repeatedly, what kind of friend would you be to stand by and let him keep falling without saying anything?"

"If I said something, he may not like it. I might be afraid of rocking the boat. I don't know, Gramps. How can you help friends who are screwing up?"

"The same way you would like to be supported."

"I'd like people to listen, and not judge me."

"I understand, Dillon. If we allow friends to be imperfect, and we do not condemn them for it, then it creates a safe space."

"I know I brought a lot of problems with me when I came here. Thank you for putting up with me, Grandfather. Your friendship has helped me incredibly."

"It has been my pleasure, Dillon. Now that your

insight and awareness are developing, your friends will not have to call you on your blind spots. You will call yourself on them. Of course you can still get together with friends you feel safe with and discuss things you may be struggling with. Friends can be a good sounding board to help clarify issues for you."

"I'm going to be careful who I choose to be my friends. It might be easy to get sidetracked."

"Choosing friends who support our journey toward developing greater insight and wisdom sure makes life easier. Picture a road before you, Dillon. You are walking toward a bright light. The purpose of your journey is to get closer to that light. You are on your path. You are walking steady along your path and you have company. These are friends who have their own paths, but they share the main road with you that leads to the light. They cannot walk your path, and you cannot walk theirs, but you share the road that ultimately leads to the same destination. These friends are good company. They may stumble along the way, just as you might. You can help pick each other up, but you have to walk your own path. Now, this road, Dillon, has many diversions."

"Do you mean side roads, or dead ends that lead you away from the main road? And U-turns that lead you in the opposite direction?"

"Yes. You may even end up at the county dump. Dillon, let's be realistic. You are going to get sidetracked from time to time. There are lessons to learn on these off-track adventures. That is okay because it is all a part of the journey. There are always lessons in what we call mistakes."

"And the key," I said, "is to figure out what the lessons mean and get back on the main road."

"Right. At times you will forget this. Wake up, get your bearings, get back on the road and keep your eyes on the light. Life will support you in reaching the destination we share."

"It feels good to have a sense of direction," I said.

"I know just what you mean, Dillon. I really enjoy sharing the main road with you."

36

HEALING WOUNDS

When I woke the next morning Grandfather was busy hauling boxes out of a back room in the cabin. He said he was moving them out to the new storage shed we had built. I offered to help.

"Great!" he said, heading out the door with an armload of old shoeboxes. I picked up a big cardboard box and the bottom of the box gave out, dropping the entire contents to the floor. I taped the box back together and began repacking it. I came across an old black-and-white snapshot of Grandfather Sage as a young man, propped up in a hospital bed and surrounded by a bunch of other young guys in military uniforms.

"I didn't know you'd been in a war, Gramps," I said, when he came back in. "What happened to you?"

"I was wounded pretty badly, Dillon. I was in that hospital for three months. That picture was taken just before I was released and sent home." He sat down while I finished packing the box.

"You know, Dillon, at times life itself seems like a battle. And, along the way, we get wounded."

"I know what you mean. I feel like I have wounds that haven't healed."

"We each have our own unique set of wounds. We all have our own stories. When we do not heal our wounds, we carry them around with us and they affect how we see things, and how we feel and react to life."

"Wounds come from many sources," he continued. "They may develop if we do not feel the nurturing and support we would like to have as we grow. If we feel betrayed or violated we develop wounds. People who have been cruel to us are often mean because they themselves are very wounded."

"Are you saying their meanness is a reaction from their hurt and wounded self?"

"Yes, that's it. Why else would they act that way?"

"Grandfather, I feel my oldest wounds are wounds of rejection. They're also wounds of feeling I'm not good enough, as if there's something I should be doing better, and I don't even know what that something is."

"I am glad to hear you say that, Dillon. It is a big step to begin examining our wounds. Are you aware that it is taking a certain amount of energy to hold onto those wounds? You are having to hold a lid down on them, you know."

"What do you mean, 'hold a lid down?' "

"Look inside, and you will feel it for yourself."

As I turned my attention inward, I realized I did seem to have a storage space with a lid on it holding down unresolved parts of myself. This is where my wounds are stored, I thought.

"You're right," I said. "I'm holding down a lot of stuff. You gotta be nuts, Gramps, if you think I'm going down in the basement to look at that stuff."

"You know, if our basement foundation is shaky it affects the solidity of the building."

"But I don't think you understand! If I ever took that lid off I might go over the edge."

"Why is that?"

"My father and all of his put-downs are there. The only emotion I ever felt from him was anger. Whenever anything went wrong he made me feel it was my fault. Now I feel it was my fault he died. Bill's down there, too. He died because I gave him my seat. There's a part of me that feels so raw I just want to cover it up. You're crazy if you think I'm going to take that lid off. There's no telling what might happen."

"Who said anything about taking the lid off, Dillon? You're just poking around with a flashlight. It would not be very smart to jump in when you have not tested the waters. You have a brick wall built up around that part of yourself, and it is there for a good reason. It has a function and has served you in the past. I just question whether or not that brick wall is serving you now."

"I've already taken down some of those bricks, but there's no way I'm going to remove the whole wall. I'd feel unprotected."

"I understand, Dillon. It is important to feel protected. Again, I just question whether that brick wall is the best type of protection. It is a lonely and isolated type of shield. It blocks the exchange of intimacy. There are better ways to protect yourself. The brick wall is quite cumbersome to carry around, and sitting on that lid takes a lot of energy."

"Well, what do we do with the wounds?" I asked.

"There is a way to defuse them. Resolving our wounds can serve us by enhancing our insight and teaching us many valuable lessons."

"How do we heal them?"

"One way is to honor and respect the hurt and wounded parts of ourselves. This allows us to look at the wounds and face them rather than hide from them. When you have physical wounds you clean them. Likewise, you begin to cleanse your mental and emotional wounds. Wounds are like constricted aspects of ourselves. They hide in the shadows and show their faces in unexpected ways. They show up in our hurts and our defenses, and in the ways our buttons get pushed. They color our vision. Emotions arise. They may range from getting angry with little cause, to feeling easily hurt, aloof or inadequate. When you attempt to get a closer look at the wounds, they may retreat and hide in your shadow. Fear is their food. When you get defensive or hurt, that energy may feed your wounds, and they thrive even more."

"So, you're saying that by acknowledging and honoring the wounds we get to know them better."

"Yes, Dillon. It becomes more difficult for them to hide in the shadows. It is as if you learn to call their names and you get to see their wounded faces and the scars they bear."

"Then what do you do?"

"We heal and dissolve them with compassion. We parent the wounds and provide them nurturing support."

"Grandfather, if we nurture and support them, won't that give them energy to grow?"

"Actually, Dillon, it works just the opposite. Your support and nurturing compassion bring them out of the shadows and into the light. It is in your nurturing light that they heal. Their scars soften. You bathe them in warmth just as a loving mother holds her newborn baby. You assure them that everything is okay."

"Then what happens?"

"The wounds begin to dissolve. But they will not dissolve all at once. Some of the wounds are deep, and it takes time to peel away the layers."

"It sounds like a lengthy process," I said.

"Dillon, you have already begun to dissolve your wounds. Just your ability to talk openly about them means the layers are softening. When the time is right, you will face the fire and penetrate the veil."

"What veil?"

"The veil that keeps you feeling separate, rather than connected to your soul. The veil creates the illusion of your being separate from the whole. You have come a long way, Dillon. Remember – the fun has just begun. Now let's get the rest of these boxes out of here so you can move into your new room."

"My new room?" I asked in surprise. I'd been sleeping on a cot in the hallway since I'd arrived. I walked over to the window and looked out at a fantastic view of the mountain ridges to the north. Tears began to well in my eyes. "Thank you very much, Grandfather." He gave me a hug and we hauled out the last few boxes.

As I moved my things into my new room, I had the feeling I was making a new start in life. The room, even though it was small, looked bare with only my cot and a small chest in it. The room was like me, it seemed – practically empty and waiting to be filled with good things. Now I'm beginning to think like Grandfather, I thought, laughing at myself.

37

I CAN

I got up one morning and couldn't find Grandfather. I wandered down to the river and strolled upstream toward the waterfall, and there he was, doing his dance with nature. He would move his arms and legs about in a slow rhythm, as if he were telling a story with his body. One of the things that most fascinated me about him was how healthy he was. He was very agile. He moved his body very gracefully, and had endless energy.

"That's some dance you're doing there, Grandfather."

"Well, get up off that rock and come over here. It's time you learned how to dance with nature."

"I can't do that."

"What do you mean, you can't?"

"I can't do what you're doing."

"Well, then, that's that, Dillon."

"Aren't you even going to try to teach me?"

"I do not think that is a good idea. It is a waste of my time."

"Now you sound like my father. You don't believe in me."

"No, Dillon. What I'm hearing is you do not believe in the fullness of your own potential."

"I think I'm doing fairly well," I said.

"Yes, you are. But I just heard you tell me 'I can't do that.' If you believe you can't, then you can't. Say you can't; say you can. Either way you will be right. Is it a good investment of my energy to attempt to teach you something

115

you have already convinced yourself you can't do? You have failed before you even started."

"I know. It's a weed. This type of self-talk is a sabotage. It's like planting a seed that bears the fruit of failure."

"Yes. It is important to keep your field of possibilities open. When you close your field, you stagnate."

"Okay, Grandfather. I am open to learning and I can learn!"

"Excellent! Dance class begins tomorrow, Dillon."

As we walked back to the cabin, I told Grandfather about a guy I know who smokes more than a pack a day of cigarettes. "He has tried to quit many times, he says, but can't do it."

"Of course not. What else would you expect? He has already declared that he can't, so how could he?"

"Well, what would you say, Grandfather?"

"I'd say, 'My previous attempts were not successful. Now I will be successful. I can do it.' This, Dillon, creates room to cultivate success. There is, though, something faulty in the statement, 'I can quit smoking.' "

"What's that?"

"If you quit something, what does that make you?"

"A quitter?"

"That's right. And if you do not like to feel like a quitter, then you are lacking the motivation to really stop."

"What would you say then?"

"How about 'I can honor my lungs' and 'I choose to honor my lungs.' "

"That makes sense," I said. "If you honor your lungs, you choose not to smoke. I'm still amazed at how our self-talk can be such a powerful force in our lives. It's like our brains are biocomputers."

"And what do you think makes up the software?"

"Our thoughts. We are running our own program," I said.

"Yes, Dillon, and many people are unaware that the outcome they experience in life is directly related to their input."

"Our thoughts are the input," I added. "We're continuously entering new input into our biocomputer. We're programming new software."

"But we also have a hard drive that stores old software, Dillon."

"I feel like you've been downloading new software into my computer."

"Yes. And just as important, we have deleted some of your outdated programming. Guess what would happen if it remained buried on your hard drive?"

"The software would keep running and affect the way I feel and act."

"Exactly, Dillon. What is disconcerting is the software runs without your permission or conscious awareness."

"I'm ready to get rebooted," I said.

"I know you are. And I would like you to enter in some software today."

"What's that?"

" 'I will be patient as my process unfolds.' "

"Okay, I just entered it. Let me save it before I lose the file."

38

RHYTHM

The next morning I found Grandfather at the waterfall again, doing his dance routine. He called me over.

"The key, Dillon," he said, "is to allow the flow of movement to unfold from your center as an extension of your harmony."

"But I don't know the sequence of the movements."

"Neither do I."

"Then how do you do it?"

"I allow them to unfold spontaneously. All you have to do is tune into the rhythm of your body and the nature around you, and you will feel and see the rhythmic movement of life." He spread his arms and began to sway and move in slow circles. "The branches of the trees dance with the wind as the grass sways in the breeze. The day gracefully changes to night and the night gracefully welcomes the day. The seasons move in a flowing rhythm. The moon plays with the tides of the oceans. Our garden gives thanks to the rain. Life has rhythm, Dillon. When you are in rhythm with life, you are in harmony."

"Why do I feel some type of resistance that keeps me from flowing?"

"Dillon, you are concerned with what others think. Your movement is not unfolding from your center. It is coming from the corner of your eye."

"The corner of my eye?"

"You know what I mean. Think back to the last time you danced."

"You're right. I felt self-conscious. I was comparing myself to everyone else."

"Do you think the trees and the birds are concerned about how you look? Do you think they are judging you?" he grinned. "Why don't you ask them for approval, Dillon, so you can stop looking out the corner of your eye?"

"They gave me a rave review," I joked. "They think I'm cool."

"You are full of yourself, aren't you?"

"Okay, Grandfather. I believe I'm in the right mindset now." I told myself there was no need to be self-conscious. My field of vision opened and, without focusing on any one thing, I was able to see everything. I began to move spontaneously. My movements became an expression of what I was feeling at each moment.

"Wow. That was powerful," I said afterwards. "Thanks for teaching me."

"I didn't teach you anything. You simply allowed yourself to be."

"I felt I was part of the rhythm of life."

"Our movements, Dillon, become an expression of our harmony. Whether we are walking, talking or rocking in a chair, we carry our rhythm with us. And if we are in harmony that rhythm becomes part of the flow."

"One other thing, Grandfather."

"Yes?"

"I thought I saw you looking out the corner of your eye."

"You're right, Dillon. I wanted to see how you looked. I was comparing myself to you and totally lost my rhythm."

"Oh, sure. You think I'm gonna buy that one."

Grandfather also taught me a method of circulating energy throughout my body. Thousands of years ago, he said, great sages were able to map out the flow of energy in their own bodies. The system of acupuncture developed from the teachings of these Chinese sages. They discovered pathways in which our life energy flows, called meridians. The major meridian which runs down the front of the body is called the conception vessel, or the functional meridian. The major meridian on the back of the body is the governing meridian.

Grandfather explained how to join the two meridian channels together in a loop called 'the microcosmic orbit.' Energy follows intention, he reminded me. Through the use of intention, I learned to guide the flow of life force up my spine and then down the front of my body. The warm current flowed around and around as I observed its movement. It was wonderful to feel the same energy that sustains life moving in my own body.

Grandfather referred to these teachings as "the ancient way." He had studied with a teacher, and I felt privileged that he was sharing these ancient teachings with me.

I was beginning to realize an important part of life is learning to cultivate and manage our energy. Without this cultivation and appropriate management, one cannot live in harmony. We become emotionally drained, or burned out, if we do not manage our energy properly. It's like driving a car, and not knowing how to fill up the gas tank.

39

SOLUTION

We were walking along the river one afternoon when we heard a screeching sound above us. We looked up, but could see only a patch of blue sky through the treetops. Grandfather said it was the unmistakable call of the bald eagle, something he'd rarely heard in that part of the woods.

"The sounds of nature are the voices of God's artwork, Dillon. They offer us wonderful gifts."

"What kinds of gifts?"

"You will learn to recognize them over time. The sounds of the songbirds offer us a gift. The sound of the ocean waves offer healing energy. The sound of the gushing river nourishes us, and the waterfall touches our souls. You may receive the gifts of God's artwork only when you truly listen. I mean, not just listening with one ear while you are engaged in other thoughts, but becoming completely absorbed in the sound, to where you feel all that exists is you and the sound. When you and the sounds of God's artwork merge, you feel the rhythm of life."

We sat down at a place where the river narrowed to about half its width. A small set of rapids rushed over the rocks.

"It is easy to let go of your thoughts here," Grandfather said. "The flowing water carries them away." We sat for a long time watching the water bubble over the rocks. I became absorbed in the cleansing sound of the river.

We heard the cry of the eagle again, and this time, when we looked up we saw them. Grandfather pointed out a young eagle following its parent. They circled directly above us, then flew away, following the river upstream. I watched them in awe.

"Come with me, Dillon."

"Where are we going, Grandfather?"

"I am taking you to my favorite healing place."

We climbed the rocks to the top of the waterfall and followed the river upstream. Oak and willow trees branched out over the water from both sides of the river, creating a canopy. As I looked ahead, a huge boulder caught my eye. I felt magnetically drawn to it.

"You are feeling the magic, Dillon. It is no coincidence you feel drawn to that boulder. That is where we are going."

As we approached the boulder I could feel its presence. "This may sound crazy," I said, "but I get the feeling this boulder knows we're here." He laughed.

"How do you know it doesn't, Dillon?" We climbed up and sat on the top of the boulder. "I come here from time to time. Solution helps me in many ways."

"Grandfather, who is Solution?"

"You felt Solution's presence when you approached her, Dillon. Now you are sitting in her lap."

"Do you mean you think this rock is alive?" I asked.

"It is somewhat difficult to explain my relationship with Solution. To me, she has a presence as real as your presence. Over the years I have come here during times when I was confused, or seeking solutions to difficult situations. And I have come here many times when I felt called to experience deeper insight."

"What do you do when you come here?"

"I sit upon her lap, like we are now, and contemplate whatever it is that I might be struggling with or attempting to sort out. She offers me inspiration. She has been quite a gracious host for all these years. To me, she is an expression of God's artwork."

"I can see that, Grandfather. She sure is a wonderful expression of nature. How did she get the name 'Solution?' "

"One day I asked her what her name was. I sat in silence and, in my mind, I heard a sweet voice whisper, 'I am Solution.' That is what I have been calling her ever since."

"Does Grandmother Prema know about Solution?"

"Yes, she does, Dillon. She does not come here, though. She has her own boulder friend she visits."

"It sounds like you've never brought anyone here before. I feel like I'm invading a private relationship."

"That's sensitive of you, Dillon, and I appreciate your courtesy. But I have brought you here for a reason. You are here so I can introduce you to Solution. The two of you have already become acquainted and I am happy I chose to share this special place with you."

"But this is your place."

"Well, Dillon, my time on this planetary school-house is limited. I will be leaving the earth long before you. But Solution will still be here, waiting to assist you. If you find yourself struggling with an issue, or just feeling stuck, you can come and sit in Solution's lap and she will offer you support. You can also come here to meditate and deepen your connection to your soul. Some of my most profound spiritual experiences have taken place right in this spot."

"I don't know what to say, Grandfather. Thank you for offering to share this special place with me. I think I'll be spending some time here, too."

"In time your relationship with her will grow, Dillon, and you will treasure her as a dear friend."

"I feel at peace here," I said. "I don't know what

my friends would think though, if they knew I was developing a relationship with a rock."

"They may think it sounds silly, Dillon. Unfortunately they have forgotten."

"Forgotten what?"

"Most people have forgotten they were in communication with the angels long before they could speak. Look into a baby's eyes and you will see that baby is connected to the angels. Do not bother with what others think. Your relationship with Solution is your business."

When we got up to leave, I said good-bye to Solution. As I walked away, I had a feeling I'd made a connection with a special friend I knew I would see again.

40

I AM BITTEN

I was gathering some large rocks to use in rebuilding a retaining wall behind the cabin one day when I uncovered a big, black timber rattler. I had rolled over a rock and was getting ready to lift it and before I knew what was happening, the snake coiled and struck, leaving two marks in my wrist.

I panicked. Oh no! I'm going to die! I thought. I ran as fast as I could, yelling to Grandfather, who was in the front yard. "Get me to a hospital!" I screamed. He came running toward me.

"Tell me what's the matter, Dillon!" I showed him the marks in my wrist and told him I'd been bitten by a black timber rattler.

"Dillon, can we wait 'til after lunch? I'm starving. How about if I make us some sandwiches and a salad, and we can go to the hospital after that?"

"Are you crazy? I could be dead by then! I might lose my arm! I feel the poison spreading through my body!"

"I knew a guy who was bitten by a rattlesnake, Dillon. It took him four hours to get to a hospital, and he was just fine. An extra half hour for us to eat won't make a difference."

"What's wrong with you, man? This is serious! I can't believe you're not even concerned!"

"Well, now, come to think of it, Dillon, your running to find me was not a good idea. That can cause the poison to spread faster. Maybe you're right. We better get to the hospital quick. Before we go, though, I know of one thing that might fix you right up." He took me into the shed and pointed to an old wooden box. Part of a side panel was missing.

"There's some medicine in that box, Dillon," he said. "Go get it quickly!"

I opened up the top of the box and screamed, nearly jumping out of my skin. Grandfather reached down and grabbed a four-foot long snake behind the head. He pulled it out of the box and started walking toward me. I started to run.

"Don't run, Dillon!" he yelled. "You'll spread the poison! Trust me."

"Stay away from me! You're a lunatic!"

"You know, Dillon, you are not the first person who has told me that. Look at the snake's tail. What do you see?"

"It's just a tail, Gramps," I said frantically.

"Well, in order for a rattlesnake to be a rattlesnake, it has to have rattles. You are looking at a black snake, which is not poisonous. There are no black timber rattlers around here. The rattlesnakes are brown and have a unique pattern. They also have rattles. These black snakes are my friends. They eat mice. This mama black snake has been in my shed for many years. Here, come and hold her."

"No, thanks. I've had enough of snakes for one day," I said, feeling both embarrassed and relieved. "Say, weren't you going to make some sandwiches, Gramps?"

41

LIFE CAN BE THE REWARD

"What are you building now, Gramps?" I found him out in the shed, whistling a tune as he cut and sanded some boards.

"New bat houses, Dillon. I like to keep as many bats as I can in the area."

"Well, it looks like you're enjoying yourself." I noticed he had a few bat houses completed. "And you're doing a fine job as well, I see."

"Have you ever had a job, Dillon?"

"Sure. I've stocked shelves in a supermarket and I've washed dishes in a restaurant."

"What did you like most about working?"

"Getting paid, of course."

"Oh? Why did you like to get paid?"

"Why would I work if it wasn't for the pay?"

"So, Dillon, your pay is your reward, and work is what you have to do to get it."

"That's right."

"And what do you do when you get paid?"

"Well, I go to the movies, or buy a pizza, or something like that."

"How long does the movie last?"

"About two hours."

"How long does it take to eat your pizza?"

"I can eat half a pie in ten minutes when I'm hungry."

"Which takes more time? The work or the reward?"

"What do you mean?"

127

"Your two-hour movie and ten-minute pizza take a lot less time than working all week to get a paycheck."

"Well, I never really thought of it like that, but I do see your point."

"Most of us have been conditioned from a young age to seek rewards. We have to figure out how to stop separating work from rewards."

"But what's wrong with rewards?"

"There is nothing wrong with rewards. The problem is in living our lives only to enjoy the rewards."

"Because rewards are short-lasting in comparison to what we have to go through in order to get them?"

"Yes. We have been conditioned to perform tasks not for the enjoyment or appreciation of the process, but for the reward that follows."

"So the problem with having the reward as our focus is that we miss the enjoyment of the process itself," I said.

"That's right. One of the keys to a fulfilling life is overcoming the distinction between that which you consider a chore and that which you consider a reward. Your reward is not just seeing your work completed. It becomes rewarding to be mindfully engaged in your work as well."

"I've experienced that, too, come to think of it. You're right. I remember mowing the lawn and looking at my watch every few minutes because I couldn't wait to get it over with. I was feeling rushed. But then another time when I mowed the grass I really got into it and had a lot of fun, even though it was hard work. I felt good about it."

"Life becomes much more entertaining when we stop separating work from rewards, Dillon. Rewards provide only temporary pleasure. If you have not figured that out, much of your life will seem like a burden. Do you know what happens if you indulge in a pleasure long enough?"

"It will lose its attraction."

"Yes, and it can even become boring after a while. But as we learn to be centered and mindful of all that we do, life becomes rewarding in itself. We lose the distinction between work, chores and rewards. We live not only to seek pleasure..."

"We live to live."

"Right, Dillon!"

42

LIFE RESPONDS

We were shoveling compost into a new garden bed on an unusually warm day and I stopped to rest for a moment. Grandfather saw me panting and called me a wimp. I could see the smirk on his face and I knew he was teasing me again. How about if I tease him a little bit for a change, I thought.

When we got back to the cabin, I challenged him to an arm wrestle. I was good at arm wrestling, and I wanted to see how he would handle losing.

We sat down at the table and our right hands embraced. I couldn't believe it. His arm locked like a bar of steel. I was unable to budge it. He calmly ate an apple with his other hand, chewing each bite slowly. I was sure he could have put my arm down with ease, but he chose to hold a locked position. After a few minutes, I told him I'd had enough. He didn't have to call me a wimp. I felt like one.

"Do you know what the problem is with focusing on what you are afraid might happen?" he asked. "You put energy into what you fear. That increases the probability of it coming true."

"Like if I'm afraid I'm going to run into a snake, it might happen?"

"Yes. You might even create a snake out of a hose. Thinking is an action, and our actions have impact. When you think, your thoughts become a part of life. The question is, what kind of impact are you creating?"

Grandfather became very serious and stared into

my eyes. I knew he had something important to say.

"Dillon, you are learning to overcome your scattered mind. You are learning to focus, which means your thoughts have more power than before. Your thoughts have more capacity to create and manifest. Remember this always: Thoughts are real. They are energy, and they exist. Life responds to our thoughts."

"I remember hearing a minister describe prayer in a similar way," I said. "He said prayer is positive thought directed toward another."

"Yes. Prayer is thought with good intention."

"And by simply thinking and feeling good will," I said, "we are living a prayerful life."

"That's right, Dillon. You become prayer in motion. You have no desire to hurt others by your words, thoughts or actions."

"What if someone does something you don't like, and you say, 'What a jerk. I hope he breaks his leg?' "

"Then immediately recognize that you have engaged in a negative thought, and put forth a new thought to cancel and neutralize the negative one. For example, you proclaim, 'I cancel that thought!' "

"You push the 'delete' button."

"Right. And that neutralizes the negative thought. When you monitor your thoughts you can determine the quality of thought you are directing toward others. When people exchange negative thoughts, they are engaging in a form of psychic warfare. They may not realize it, but they are playing in the dark, and the consequences can be damaging."

"I prefer not to play that game anymore."

"I know that, Dillon, and it makes me feel very good. We are learning to live in harmony. It is a much more rhythmic dance."

43

BE CAREFUL WHAT YOU ASK FOR

I was intrigued with the idea that thoughts are energy, and actually become more powerful when we're conscious of what we're thinking. The more aware we are of our thoughts, the more power they contain. Knowing this, I felt a responsibility to improve my thought quality.

Over the next few days I spent a lot of time alone and practiced being mindful of my thoughts. I began to find it very easy to observe my mind, as though I was in the audience of a theater, witnessing the show. I was able to step back from the drama of my thoughts. I knew that my essence, or who I really am, had to be more than my thoughts or I would not be able to observe them. "I am awareness," I thought, as I witnessed the panorama of my mind.

I understood what Grandfather had meant when he said every thought is a seed and certain emotions are the fruits they bear. I noticed when I thought about other people I had a tendency to place them in a more-than or less-than position. If I thought, "How dare he do that," I would feel myself becoming angry.

When I thought about myself, I often put myself down, or felt I was not good enough. If I thought, "I should have done better" or "I shouldn't have done that," inadequacy is the emotion that would sprout. I began to experience a fantastic feeling of freedom as I realized I am capable of choosing the thoughts I plant in the garden of my mind.

It was becoming much easier to let go of my

thoughts and enter into the stillness of being. I found it very comforting to be fully present to the moment.

I was curious, too, about what Grandfather had said about thoughts being a means of creating, or manifesting. I found him working in the shed again one afternoon and asked him if he could explain more about this.

"Sure, Dillon. Let's go for a walk, and hang up some of our new bat houses while we talk, shall we?" We walked into the woods down the hill from the cabin where it was cool and shady.

This was an area I hadn't explored much. I wandered around while Grandfather did all the work of putting up the bat houses. I found a small stream that must have fed into the river. I sat down there on a soft bed of fallen pine needles. Grandfather joined me a few minutes later.

"Our thoughts and intentions are real, Dillon," he said. "They set our lives into motion. We attract to ourselves what we create in our thought world. This type of creation is called manifestation."

"So, what manifests in our lives," I asked, "is a result of the thoughts we have previously set into motion?"

"Yes. That is a big part of it. Much of what I have accomplished in my life has come to fruition from my consciously choosing to create it; being here on this land, for instance, and my relationship with Grandmother Prema. Many of the wonderful things that have unfolded in my life have manifested as a result of my thoughts and intention. Life can be a self-fulfilling prophecy which we create from a combination of our beliefs, assumptions, and ways in which we direct our thoughts."

"Then our thoughts and beliefs are like energy magnets. What we put forth attracts people or things that resonate with our intention. I guess we should be careful what we ask for."

"That's right, Dillon. Be careful what you ask for because you just might get it. Once you have created a desire, there is a pressure to fulfill that desire. There is a risk of becoming a slave to your desires. Before you allow yourself to take on a desire, it is important to understand where it will lead you and what the consequences will be."

"But when you consciously choose to create, isn't that like creating a need or desire in your mind?"

"The difference is you choose to create without attachment. If it does not happen, it is okay. You are not attached. You ask to allow only your highest choice and the highest good to manifest. If it does not fit that criteria, you give the universe permission to cancel your order."

"Can the universe really do that?"

"Sure it can. It has changed my order many times. In fact, it has served me up some things that were completely unexpected. You see, what I sometimes thought was in my best interest was not what was really best for me, or those I was associated with. The universe helped me to see that and provided me with lessons and experiences that were more appropriate for me at the time."

"It's amazing the universe works with us this way."

"Yes, it is truly amazing, Dillon. That is the gift and support life offers us."

44

PARTNERSHIP WITH LIFE

I was beginning to see myself, and life, in a new way. Just being in nature, without television, and without radio, or even newspapers, made me realize how caught up I had always been with one distraction or another. I had now developed an appreciation for allowing the sun's movement through the sky and the natural rhythms of nature to guide my daily activities. It seemed like a whole new reality.

One day late in the afternoon I was heading back to the cabin, feeling exhilarated, but exhausted, after a full day of hiking. I stumbled over a stick in my path. I thought this was a sign that it might be a good idea to stop and rest for a few minutes. I plopped down and picked up the stick. It was about four feet long. I removed some loose bark and took out my pocketknife and carved some leaf patterns into the wood. I decided to give it to Grandfather.

I returned to the cabin to find Grandfather in the midst of laying out a fantastic dinner. He had spent the afternoon baking bread.

"I thought you might be hungry, Dillon," he smiled.

I thanked him heartily. After dinner I gave him the walking stick.

"I should be able to get around for many years to come with this," he chuckled. "Thank you, Dillon."

"And thank you, Grandfather," I said. He became quiet as he examined my carving on the stick.

"When I was younger, Dillon," he said after a few minutes, "I was comfortable with giving, but my problem was I did not feel comfortable receiving. I had to learn to be open to receiving, and as I learned to do this I was able to find a deeper level of harmony within myself. I discovered it is important to have a balance between giving and receiving."

"What happens if you only give?" I asked.

"You are not taking care of yourself properly. You give all your time and energy away, and that leaves you with a lack of time to care for yourself. People who over-give become like martyrs."

"What about those who just want to receive? That creates a problem, too, doesn't it? I've known people who are so self-centered they think only their life matters."

"I know what you mean, Dillon. Being around people like that is not much fun. They want more and more, but never seem satisfied."

"I guess I've had times when I was self-centered, too. I'd get angry if I didn't get what I wanted."

"Me too, Dillon. We can get caught up in expecting life to always conform to our whims. I have learned the more preoccupied we are with having things our way, the more frustration and misery we experience."

"So, Grandfather, how do we find a balance then, between giving and receiving?"

"We give, and we serve, but at the same time it is important we remain open to receiving."

"I used to think the only way to give was to give money, and if you didn't have money, you had nothing to give," I said.

"Financial giving is a way one can serve. You can also serve by giving your time, or by putting forth positive thoughts and intention. There are many expressions of service and you will find your own unique way to serve."

"What do you think I have to offer the world?"

"The greatest thing you can give, Dillon, is your soul shining to greet everyone you come into contact with. Then you are helping to lighten the load. Your peaceful presence helps to clear the air of its denseness. You provide a balance to the darker thoughts which also pervade space. When one is in harmony, their harmony helps to create harmony in others. What a great gift to offer the universe!"

"Giving, then, is a way of returning to life the gifts that you have received."

"That is a wonderful way to put it, Dillon. Life will return to you many-fold that which you have given to life."

"We're not living just to get something out of life then."

"Right, Dillon. We are not here to conquer. We are here to work with life as a partner. It is a sacred partnership that develops when we work in cooperation with life for the benefit of ourselves and the benefit of others."

"You didn't tell me yet, why you had trouble receiving."

"Well, when I was growing up, Dillon, a part of me became programmed to think I was not worthy of receiving. I was conditioned to think it was selfish. I thought if I received it would cause an inconvenience. This blocked the flow of my consciously receiving the gift of Mother Earth energy."

"How did you get over it?"

"When I began to heal my wounds and wake up from the trances of everyday life I started to feel worthy of both giving and receiving."

"It sounds simple. It seems like when we're in harmony, the balance of giving and receiving comes naturally."

"Yes, Dillon. Naturally and effortlessly."

45

OUR EYES SEE ONLY A GLIMPSE OF REALITY

The long hot summer days made it necessary to water the garden a great deal more than usual. I was watering one evening when Grandfather came out. He strolled slowly up and down the rows with his hands clasped behind him, stopping occasionally to examine a particular plant.

"Dillon," he called out from the far corner of the garden, "these watermelon vines would like some more water!"

"I already watered them, Grandfather!" I called back.

"I can see that, but they would really appreciate a little more water!"

"Okay! No problem! Tell them I'll be right over!" I dragged the hose back down the row to where Grandfather was kneeling next to the watermelons.

"If we pick this larger one, Dillon, the smaller ones will be happier, and do better."

"I can see their smiling faces already," I joked.

"Oh, yes," he said, thumping the larger one with his knuckle. "Do you hear that, Dillon? This one is ripe and ready for consumption. We can have some when you are finished with the watering." He headed back toward the cabin, smiling, and cradling the watermelon in his arms as if it were a newborn baby.

When I had finished the watering I found Grandfather on the front porch in his rocking chair admiring the watermelon he had placed on the table next to him.

"It sure is a beauty, isn't it, Dillon?"

"The prettiest I've seen. So, tell me, Grandfather, how did you know the watermelon plants were so thirsty tonight? You could see the soil was soaked."

"There are ways to see without using our eyes, Dillon. Our eyes, ears, nose and tongue are sensory organs we use to take in data from the world. We hear things, smell things, taste things and see things. Right?"

"Right."

"Our perceptions can be limited to what we are physically capable of perceiving. And if our sensory organs are limited, that means our perception of the world is limited."

"Well, I know our sense of hearing is limited," I said. "My cousin had a dog whistle. When I blew it, his dog could hear it, but we couldn't."

"Right, Dillon. Our ears hear only certain frequencies within a particular bandwidth of frequencies. Our eyes see light waves only within a certain frequency range. When something is out of the range of your eyes capacity to see it, you might think it doesn't exist."

"So when people say, 'I'll believe it when I see it,' they may not realize they're limiting themselves to what they can see."

"Yes, and there is more going on in this universe than meets the eye. We all have an inner eye, Dillon, we call the 'eye of intuition' that allows us to sense hidden aspects of reality we cannot see with our eyes, or perceive with our other senses. The eye of intuition is connected to that deep part of ourselves that understands everything around us, including our physical bodies, is a vibration of energy."

"I remember reading a magazine article about quantum physics," I said. "It said matter is not really a substance, and 99.9 percent of every atom is empty space.

Subatomic particles moving at lightning speed are energy in a state of vibration."

"Yes, everything is energy and everything has a different vibration. In the material world things differ in substance due to energy patterns vibrating in their own unique way. The ancients were aware that life is a dance of energy, and your intuitive self perceives life as energy. Every thought, word or feeling has its own vibration."

"I call them good vibes and bad vibes," I said.

"And we sense these vibes, Dillon, oftentimes without awareness, and they affect the decisions we make. Of course we can develop our ability to sense vibration, and become consciously aware of what we are sensing. That helps us to choose more wisely."

"There was a guy who tried to become friends with me. I didn't know anything about him, but something in me didn't like his vibes. I'm glad I followed my feelings because I found out later he was a major drug dealer and a thief. His friends got busted with him."

"Your intuitive eye was looking out for you that time, Dillon." Grandfather sliced open the watermelon and handed me a piece, staring at me as I took a bite. "What does it taste like, Dillon?"

"It tastes good."

"But can you describe the taste so I will know what you are tasting?"

"It's sweet, ya know, and juicy. Like a melon, ya know?"

He sighed and shook his head. "I don't know what you mean. I guess I will have to taste it myself," he said, slicing off a huge piece. I laughed at him, wondering what he was trying to show me this time.

"Language can be limiting as well, Dillon."

"I guess language can take you only so far."

"Awakening to the fullness of the moment and the joy of our inner being is an experience beyond words. There is unity within the diversity of life. Since everything is energy, all the parts are interconnected to the whole. Language is the means by which we communicate with one another, but it is limited in helping us to experience the deeper reality, or essence, of our soul."

"So, Grandfather, the information we take in through our limited senses we translate into words, and discuss as if we're seeing the whole picture."

"Language is important, or we would not have had the wonderful conversations we have had, but until we develop our ability to feel and sense energy, Dillon, we are looking at a very limited picture."

"Sometimes we communicate without words."

"You're right, Dillon. That is my favorite kind of communication. I've been thinking about taking a period of silence, and now seems like a good time to begin."

46

YES OR NO?

When I got up the next morning I found Grandfather sitting at the kitchen table, as usual, drinking his tea.

"Good morning, Grandfather."

No response. I realized he was still in his silent mode. I headed out the door and down to the river.

I loved to meditate by the river early in the morning and see the sun come up over the hills. This had become part of my morning routine. Then I would go back to the cabin for breakfast.

I didn't see Grandfather again until later that afternoon. He still wasn't talking.

"Okay," I said. "Enough is enough. You haven't talked all day. I'm concerned you're serious about this vow of silence."

He picked up a notepad and wrote, "You may ask me one question. If it is an important question, I will speak. If it is not a worthy question, my lips are sealed."

"Oh, come on! I don't know what to ask you. Quit goofing around."

Then he wrote, "Be clear before you ask."

I didn't know if he was serious, or not, but I thought I'd better come up with something good. I decided to quiet my mind and ask my inner voice for guidance in coming up with a relevant question. After a short period of time I heard an "ah-ha."

"Okay, Grandfather," I asked, "how do I know a 'yes' means yes and a 'no' means no?"

He stared into my eyes for nearly a minute. I could tell he liked my question. Then he gave me a thumbs-down and turned around and headed for the door. I immediately felt myself go into a fight/flight response and my breathing became restricted.

Then he said, "Great question. Follow me."

I was perplexed. I followed him outside and we sat down on the front steps.

"Dillon, you asked a good question. How do you know a 'yes' means yes and a 'no' means no? If you had felt my energy, you would have known I thought your question was a good one. I gave you an affirmative response through my vibration, yet you chose only to see my thumbs-down response."

"Well, at first I thought you liked my question. I saw it in your eyes, but I didn't trust the feeling."

"If you had, Dillon, you would have known that my thumbs-down was a joke because I had already expressed my appreciation of your question."

"What you're saying is, trust your gut feelings."

"That's it. Close your eyes and let me give you an example of a statement you know is a 'yes.' Two plus two equals four. Can you feel a part of you inside saying 'yes?' "

"Yes, I can."

"How about three plus three equals seven? Can you feel yourself saying 'no?' "

"Yes, I can feel that, too."

"So when you ask yourself a question like, 'Is this good for me?' or 'Is this a good choice?' look inside and see what your gut is telling you. Does it feel like 'two plus two equals four,' or does it feel like 'three plus three equals seven?' Combine the response you felt with common sense, and you will have your answer. Learn to trust your inner knowing."

"It is important to develop your sense of discrimination," he continued, "so that you know what is in your best interest and supports your highest good."

"It seems to me learning to trust that response takes practice."

"Yes, it does. It means developing your instinct."

"You mean like the instinct animals have?"

"Yes, a similar type of knowing that is beyond words."

"Because you're sensing energy and vibrations."

"Right."

"Well, I'm glad you've come out of your silence, Grandfather. And my instinct tells me you like to play games with my head."

"Good instinct, Dillon!" he laughed.

47

GROUNDING AND CLEARING SPACE

One day late in the afternoon we were surprised by a sudden thunderstorm. I had been splitting firewood while Grandfather stacked it in the woodshed. He was teaching me the words to an old-time mountain tune he remembered from his childhood. People would often sing, he said, to keep their energy levels up while they worked long days in the summertime.

We were singing loudly, and laughing at the nonsensical lyrics when the wind picked up suddenly, blowing in lots of massive dark clouds. We heard a clap of thunder and saw a lightning bolt hit the ground. I dropped the ax. Grandfather dropped an armload of wood, and we both ran as fast as we could for the cabin.

After we had caught our breath and relaxed for a few minutes Grandfather disappeared into the huge storage closet off the kitchen. I sat looking out through the screen door and remembered the night I had spent alone out in the woods during the lightning storm. What an ego I'd had! I shook my head. It was almost unbelievable to me how my perceptions had changed since then. Grandfather walked back into the room carrying a small wooden box.

"I feel like I've begun to wake up from a dream," I said. "The funny thing is, I had no idea I was dreaming. When I look back on the way I used to think and act, I'm not sure who that person was."

"Always keep in mind, Dillon, that God is not through with you yet. Yes, you may look back and see that the way you were is much different than the way you are now. But, guess what? This process will continue throughout your lifetime. In the future you will look back again, and feel as if this time was a dream. The purpose of your life's journey is to continuously discover deeper levels of insight and wisdom." He opened the box and pulled out a chessboard.

"Well! It looks like playing chess is going to be part of my life today," I grinned. "I think it's only fair to warn you, though. I'm pretty good at it."

Grandfather just smiled and set up the chess pieces.

He won the first game in less than ten minutes. The second game lasted a few minutes longer, but he won again. The thunderstorm had passed over by the time we were on our third game, but a steady rain was falling. I was contemplating what Grandfather's next move would be.

"Checkmate," he said.

"How did you do that again?! Not one of our games has lasted more than fifteen minutes! This is so frustrating!"

"If frustration is what you would like to create with your time, Dillon, feel free to elaborate. Would you like to throw something or break anything?"

"No, I'm not that pissed."

"Well, the clock is ticking, Dillon."

"What do you mean by that?"

"Every second you are getting one second closer to your physical death. What do you choose to create with your time? Will you create inner harmony, and add a healing fragrance to planetary space, or will you create a lot of frustrated energy which pollutes space?"

"Okay. I get the picture."

"Dillon, have you ever walked into a room where you could feel that it had been contaminated with negative mental energy?"

"Yes. The room felt very heavy. I didn't feel like staying there."

"That is because the energy of that space did not resonate with your vibration. A lot of emotional dumping may have taken place there. Certain spaces can be carrying a lot of constrictive energy. Your energy field can pick up unwanted debris just like a white coat gets dirty in a polluted smog."

"Then what would you do if you had to stay there?"

"You can change the vibration of the space."

"How do you do that?"

"You balance yourself by grounding and moving into your center. Your harmony will clear the space. If not completely, it will at least create some clear space around you."

"What you're saying is we're going to pick up negative energy from people or places, and if we're grounded we're able to discharge negative energy?"

"Exactly. Dark space becomes light when you turn the light on, doesn't it?"

"Wow! I see what you mean. But if we fear the dark space, our fear contributes to the dark space, making it even darker. So our protection is keeping ourselves grounded and in harmony?"

"If you are not grounded, you may pick up that negative energy and carry it around with you, and then you run the risk of dumping your pent-up emotions on other people, or holding it in where it might fester."

"I can see how negative energy can be harmful, but how do you ground it?"

"With your intention. Your intent is to ground non-productive energy, just as a grounding rod grounds electrical overcharges. You vent the overcharge into Mother Earth rather than dumping it on a loved one, or blowing things out of proportion."

"Isn't that harmful to Mother Earth?"

"She can handle it, Dillon. She knows how to recycle. She turns dead leaves into compost so we can grow vegetables. She evaporates mud puddles and they become clouds which return as rain to the fields. She will recycle your negative energy and support you with an abundance of nurturing energy that is always available to you."

"And not only is it for our own protection," Grandfather continued, "living in harmony is a service to the planet because your lighter vibration helps to transmute those cruder vibrations. Remember – energy cannot be created or destroyed, but it can be transformed, just like the presence of the sun transforms a patch of ice to flowing water."

"So if everything is connected, and our vibrations are influencing the universe, then at every moment we are having an effect on life?"

"That's right. And it is important to remember to keep our feet grounded and rooted to the earth, just as a tree is rooted to the earth, and to keep our heads in the heavens. Do you know what happens if your head is in the heavens but your feet are not grounded on the earth?"

"You'd be too much of a space cadet."

"Yes. You may lack everyday practicality or common sense. What would happen if you were connected to the earth, but did not have a connection with the heavens?"

"Then you'd be too focused on the physical world, and you might become too material-minded."

"Right. Having a healthy connection to both the heavens and the earth creates balance and harmony. When you live in harmony, you contribute to the healing of planetary space. When you live in anger, depression or fear, your energy contributes to the collective negativity. So

148

when emotions come up, deal with them constructively rather than letting them take up residence."

"Well, Grandfather, I've just grounded my frustrated energy from the chess game and if I dumped any of it on you, I'm sorry."

"It's okay, Dillon. Even if you tried to dump it on me, I would not accept it. A lot of packages are sent your way. You get to choose what you would like to sign for."

48

RELIGION OR SPIRITUALITY?

Grandfather helped me to understand how both recent and old emotional charges are stored in our systems. He taught me how to do awareness exercises designed to access those constricted, or frozen, parts of myself. That stuck energy, he said, can be neutralized and transformed into pure life force. I was beginning to realize that compassion is a natural by-product of having balanced energy, and I saw my spiritual journey as a process of balancing my energy so I could have compassion and live in harmony.

I drove into town one day to get some supplies and was at the gas station filling up Grandfather's truck when I was approached by a well-dressed man in his forties. He handed me a small booklet. On the cover were the words, "Are You Going To Hell Or Heaven?" He asked me if we could talk for a moment.

I told him I believed I'd been living in Hell, and am now in the process of learning to connect with heaven and earth. He looked confused. I explained that previously my mind had created a lot of grief, but now I'm happier and more in harmony.

He gave me a look that was very familiar to me. He was coming from a better-than position, and looked at me as if I were a poor, lost soul. I didn't feel like assuming a less-than position. I looked him in the eye, and said, "I feel really good about my path. Thanks for your concern."

"But you don't understand," he said. "You must believe that. . . "

"Listen," I said. "I feel really good about where I am right now. I feel spiritually connected and I'm happy with my path. I respect where you are and I ask that you respect where I am."

He wouldn't accept that. "But," he went on, "there is only one way. . ."

His better-than position was beginning to annoy me. I could feel myself becoming rebellious, although I was also partly observing the drama and found it amusing. "I guess we don't see eye to eye on this," I said. "Have a good day."

As I reached for the door, he stepped in between me and the truck, still trying to convince me I could be saved. Finally, I said, "Look. I feel you're acting like you're superior to me. You believe only you have the truth. I'm not going to play this game with you. It's not the type of spirituality I'm interested in."

Wow, did that set him off! He insisted I take a few more of his booklets and told me he would pray for me. I shook my head as I drove away.

When I got back to Stillpoint, I handed the booklets to Grandfather. "I'm a new man!" I joked. "I know where I'm going when I die!"

"Well, I know where you are going while you are still alive!" he said, heading for the door. "Come on!"

"What are you talking about?" I asked.

"We've got trenches to dig!" he grabbed two shovels, handed one to me, and I followed him around to the back of the cabin, where runoff from the previous day's rain was streaming down the hillside. We began digging a trench to divert the excess water away from the cabin's foundation.

"Some people will try to tell you up is good, and down is evil," said Grandfather. "I believe the earth below us is beautiful!" He reached down and grabbed a handful of rich soil. An earthworm crawled between his fingers. "This is the earth that nourishes us. It provides our food. We honor the earth because she is our mother. She is a living being. The rivers are her veins and the atmosphere is her lungs. She is not an inert object. She is alive! Many people are cut off from the earth, which means they are separated from an important part of themselves. They miss out on a beautiful aspect of life. So, Dillon, what do you think the difference is between religion and spirituality?"

"Well," I replied, "religion is what you do because you believe it will keep you from going to Hell. Spirituality is when you realize you're already in Hell, and it's what you do to get out."

Grandfather burst out laughing.

"I don't understand why people fight over God," I said.

"Maybe it's because they feel a need to seek a higher position in the herd, Dillon. People may not realize they are developing a false sense of security by assuming a self-righteous, or better-than position. They believe a model that says, 'I've got the monopoly on truth. If you do not believe my interpretation of God, you are doomed.' That belief structure is very limiting."

"Like the guy I met in town. He refused to accept that I could be spiritual unless I did it exactly his way."

"Dillon, some people follow a religion but lose sight of the spiritual essence. When people get lost in ritual, dogma, or self-righteous thinking, they miss the spiritual boat."

"My parents took me to services regularly when I was younger," I said. "I couldn't make sense of it. I couldn't see how it applied to my life. I think some of the people came for social reasons. Others were there because they were afraid of what the neighbors would think if they didn't go. I know some were there because it was good for their business. But I do remember a few people who seemed to stand out because they had a glimmering look in their eyes. Come to think of it, you've also got that look."

"Guess what, Dillon? I've seen that glimmering look in your eyes, too. Religion without spirituality is empty. It is dogma and ritual without inner experience. If one does not understand the spiritual significance of the ritual, it will be a shallow experience. Remember when we talked about the main road?"

"Sure. The road that leads to the light ahead and the spirit within."

"That main road is the spiritual journey," he said. "Walking your path as you grow in wisdom and learning to live in harmony is what spirituality is all about. Spirituality is a state of being, an inner experience. It is not simply a belief structure. Spirituality is about living with integrity."

"That makes sense. What would you think if I decided not to practice the religion I grew up in?"

"It is your choice, Dillon. You may choose to participate in your religion, but if you do so, incorporate your spirituality into the religious expression. Then you will not feel shallow in your experience. If you choose not to participate, that is your choice. You live your spirituality. Life becomes your church and your integrity becomes your temple."

49

YOUR BOTTOMLINE SELF

After dinner that night Grandfather looked through the booklets I had been given by the guy at the gas station. He looked amused as he set them aside.

"Different cultures and religions have different names for God and different ways of expressing their worship, but God remains One. Always remember, Dillon, there is a unity that exists within diversity. When people forget this, they get caught up in experiencing only diversity and separation. They fight with the pieces that look different from their own. They fail to see the interconnection of the web."

"Maybe it's their wounds and their conditioning that limit their perspective. They feel separate from life."

"Exactly, Dillon. As human beings it is our responsibility to become conscious of the connection between our individual existence and the sacred fabric of which we are all a part. God is the weaver of life and each of us is a stitch in the sacred fabric."

"That's why equality is so important."

"That's right, Dillon. We look beyond people's faults and idiosyncrasies and connect with them on a soul level. We recognize that they have been created, just as we have, in the image of God."

"I've heard it said we are all children of the universe, all part of a universal family, but I had never understood what that was supposed to mean to me."

"As we become grounded in our identification as a child of the universe, our reference point shifts and an awareness of our connection to the sacred fabric becomes a conscious and continuous experience. Your bottomline identity is that you are created in the image of God and your bottomline self is the constant you that remains unchanged through all of time."

"My bottomline self?"

"It is always present, but can be realized only when we step back from all our created roles and conditioning. When we believe we *are* the roles and the identities we play, we fail to experience our original self."

"So if thoughts and emotions come and go," I said, "they cannot be the original self. If the body is always changing, that cannot be the original self."

"Dillon, the original self is the you that has always been present under the surface. It was there when you were born. It has been there through all your pain and all your pleasures. It is the constant you that is the same you here at this moment, and will be here tomorrow. All else changes, but your true self remains."

"I guess that's why learning to calm the mind is essential, if we are going to discover our true self."

"Yes. It is your birthright, Dillon, to claim this existence and to break free from all the roles and programming that attempts to convince you that you are something other than a child of God. God is in you. Your inner center, your soul, is the divine spark of God. Your inner center is the aspect of infinity that lives in you. It is your original self."

50

PLATEAU

I stood barefoot watching the waterfall early one morning while I practiced circulating energy through the various pathways in my body, as Grandfather had shown me. I could feel the earth's energy spiral up through the "bubbling spring" point in the ball of my feet, and I could feel the energy of the heavens spiraling into the crown of my head. Using intent to move the life force through the meridian channels was becoming more natural to me. I could feel these energies flow up the spine and down the front of my body. I increased the velocity and could feel the warm current moving around and around the orbital loop, almost as if it were everywhere at once.

After a while I turned around to sit down and there was Grandfather, sitting only a few yards behind me. He had caught me by surprise again.

"What a magnificent day, Grandfather! I feel very alive inside."

"You are. Your energy is flowing with less resistance. The energy body of the earth is amazing, isn't it, Dillon? It sustains millions of life forms including every blade of grass and every bird and butterfly. You are developing a conscious awareness of this nurturing energy. That bubbling spring point is a special acupuncture point that is helping you develop your capacity to ground and connect to Mother Earth energy. Just as a tree receives this nurturing energy through its roots, you are becoming aware of your connection to the earth's energy field. And you are also becoming aware of your connection to the heavens."

"I can feel there are fewer energy blockages in my body."

"That is exactly what is happening, Dillon! Your energy body is more refined and subtle. It is less dense. That is why you are experiencing an increase in the velocity of energy through your orbit. The flow of life energy in your microcosmic orbit is similar to an acupuncture treatment. As your life force flows through the meridians in your orbit, the other meridians are able to receive a healthy charge from the circulating energy. This stimulates your immune system. Frozen and constricted energy begins to dissolve. When you are ill, there is an imbalance in the flow of your energy. Depending on how your energy is constricted or stagnant, physical and mental imbalances surface."

"Can emotional wounds form these blockages in the energy body?" I asked.

"Yes. Unfinished business, limited belief systems, environmental factors and even what we eat may cause imbalances. As your energy body moves into an even more subtle vibrational level, the layers of resistance dissolve and your original self can shine through. You are already getting glimpses of this experience."

"I'm looking forward to discovering my original self."

"Remember the importance of being patient. Enjoy the process as it unfolds. You may find yourself hitting plateaus from time to time though. It may feel good, but do not get too comfortable or you may begin to stagnate."

"Are you saying when we reach a plateau we have some inner work to address?"

"That's right. By your attending to that new level of inner work, you move beyond the plateau to a more

157

integrated level of being. We shift to a more refined vibrational level as our energy flows with less resistance."

"And we get closer to our center. Right?"

"Yes. And how nice it is to get closer to the center of our being, and the sweetness of our soul." Grandfather stood up and started walking upstream. I wondered if he was going to visit Solution.

I knew layers of blocked energy within me had dissolved. I was feeling more balanced than I'd ever felt in my life. But I also felt that I had reached a plateau. I was aware of a deep layer of stuck energy within myself that seemed to have a hard shell. I sensed it was related to old emotional wounds. I remembered when Grandfather and I had talked about healing wounds. I had become scared when I felt all the hurt and anger I was storing inside. I knew a lot of those emotions were connected to my relationship with my father.

If I chose to work through this blocked energy, my spiritual growth would be accelerated. A part of me hoped, though, that if I could just ignore it, maybe it would find a way to dissolve itself.

51

SOLUTION CALLS ME

"Happy Birthday, Dillon. How does it feel to be eighteen?"

"Thanks, Grandfather. No different than it felt yesterday," I laughed. My mind flashed suddenly to all the things I had looked forward to when I turned eighteen — how I'd be free to make my own decisions, go wherever I chose and do what I liked.

"Dillon, I had a wonderful dream last night. I awoke feeling very happy."

"What was the dream about?"

"I think it would be better if I shared it with you another time."

"If you say so. What would you like to do today?"

"Why don't you give some thought to what you would like to do, Dillon."

"Well, I thought maybe we . . . "

"Dillon, you are not catching my drift."

"Well, what do you mean?" I asked.

"What I mean, Dillon, is you are being called, but you are not hearing the call."

"Who's calling me? My mother?"

"It is not your mother, Dillon. Look inside and listen for a while."

Grandfather walked away. I quieted my mind and listened. A picture of Solution came into my mind. As I thought about her, I began to feel a magnetic attraction. Yes, Solution is calling me. Or maybe I'm calling her. I decided to pay her a visit and rest upon her solid rock lap. I found Grandfather sitting on the porch.

"Grandfather, how about we go visit Solution today?"

"It is best if you visit Solution by yourself."

"But what will you do?"

"The question is, what will you do, Dillon? She has a birthday present for you if you are ready to receive it."

"Okay, I'll get ready to go."

"Plan to go for a few days, Dillon."

"What?! That's a long time!"

"You will be surprised at how time flies. I have a backpack ready for you with a tent and sleeping bag. Oh, and Dillon, be careful not to step on any rattlesnakes," he grinned.

"Thanks a lot. Do you have any other words of wisdom for me?" I joked.

"Trust the wisdom of the universe, be open, and allow the rest to unfold."

"Okay. Well, I'm off on my birthday adventure," I laughed.

As I walked my mind began to play games with me. I kept thinking I was about to step on a rattlesnake. But what, at first, looked like snakes to me, were only dead tree limbs lying on the ground.

"Why did he have to go and put that thought in my head?" I complained aloud.

As I approached Solution, I felt the same magnetic attraction begin to pull me closer. I was happy to see her, and I felt as if she were welcoming me also.

I was extremely warm from my hike and decided to go for a swim. I took my clothes off and jumped in. I felt a little self-conscious about getting out of the water. What if someone sees me? I thought. I looked around slowly at the surrounding forest, then laughed at myself, realizing the only ones who might see me were the squirrels playing in the trees. I climbed out and lay in the sun for awhile.

I spent a long time just listening to the soft sound of the flowing river and being in the peaceful stillness of the moment. I remembered what Grandfather had said as I was leaving: Trust the wisdom of the universe, be open, and allow the rest to unfold. As I contemplated these words an "ah-ha" came forth. There is something within me that is blocked, and if I can trust and be open, the rest will unfold. If I could get through that block I'd be able to move to a deeper connection with myself and rise above the limitations of the plateau I seemed to be on.

I thought about Grandfather telling me we have to be careful what we ask for because we just might get it. So, I thought, would this be in my best interest? Before I had even finished the question, a strong "YES!" came forth from deep inside. I focused all my attention on my center.

"Let me see and feel this block," I said. I felt another "ah-ha." First you are to create a safe and nurturing space so the block will show its face. I stated my intent, asking that only the highest good be manifested. I smiled and, using a method Grandfather had taught me, I sent that smiling energy into the center of my being. I felt the warmth spread from my center to the outside of my body. I spoke to the block.

"I call on you now and ask you to show me your face. Reveal yourself to me." I heard the energy block answer.

"Do you really want to know?" it asked.

"Yes, I do."

"Are you sure you really want to know?"

"Yes! I do!"

52

FACING THE FIRE

I felt something beginning to brew inside. It was as if I had a big knot under immense pressure building in my solar plexus area. The block was surfacing. I got scared. "I think I've had enough," I said to myself. The feeling subsided instantly. The pressure I'd felt building was almost completely gone.

"I'm glad that's over with," I said. "I think I'll go pick some wild berries." Then I heard a silent whisper: Trust, be open, and allow the rest to unfold. I ignored it and climbed down from Solution's lap and began looking around for a berry patch. I knew walking away was a cop-out. I had failed to face the challenge before me.

I knew if I did not return to face the fire I would remain at a plateau level. But I was fearful of facing that old bottled-up energy. What if I open a floodgate and go off the deep end? What if the rage surfaces and I cannot get it back under control? I thought I could hear Solution calling me back, like a loving mother telling her scared child that everything will be alright.

I went back and climbed up onto Solution's lap again. I took some time to center myself and created a warm, nurturing space using the inner smile again. When I had reached a place of peaceful stillness, I again called on the blocked energy.

"Show me your face. Reveal yourself to me."
"Do you really want to know?" I heard again.
"I'm ready to know."
The block began to surface. The knot of pressure

began to build in my solar plexus. I felt as if my heart was constricting.

"I think I've had enough!"

"Dillon, face your fire!"

I felt an anger, and a rage, like hot lava boiling up from a volcano. I knew what was happening was an eruption of deep wounds. It felt like pus coming out of an infection. The pus was anger and guilt and shame I had refused to acknowledge. The blocked energy that formed these wounds was hiding in the shadows because it did not feel safe in facing the fire. Now I was ready. I allowed my awareness and light to penetrate into the core of my shadow. I could see blocked layers of energy in many colors that blemished my clarity.

These wounds and blemishes came from a combination of sources: from feeling hurt and betrayed in my battles with the world, from my feelings that I had been unworthy, from my confusion over not being able to make sense of the world, and the confinement of my conditioning.

My feelings of being threatened and intimidated by my father bubbled to the surface. I had flashbacks of being blamed and punished for things I hadn't done. I remembered him hitting me and telling me over and over again that I was not good enough. I remembered asking him many times to come to my baseball games, but he never came. I grieved the wounds of my childhood and the loss of my father. I was horrified that only two days before his fatal heart attack I had told him to "drop dead." I grieved over the father-son relationship we never had.

I let out a scream that came from the pit of my gut. That scream went on and on, breath after breath. I bent over with my head between my legs. I lost all track of time, forgetting even where I was. It started to rain. I was aware of every cold drop hitting my bare skin. I lay there naked on my back, spread across Solution's lap. I began to weep and weep. My tears mixed with the raindrops and blended together in a stream that washed over my body.

I felt raw. The wounds were open and draining. I remembered a healing pool of water Grandfather had told me about, thirty yards or so upstream from where Solution rests. I walked upstream until I found it. Rocks formed a circle around the pool, which was about eight feet in diameter. I got into the pool and rested on a big flat rock under the water. When I leaned back on the rock, the water came up to my chin. I closed my eyes and began to create a nurturing space inside.

The water was like a poultice drawing toxins out of my body. I sensed these toxins were not physical poisons. They were residual energy toxins being cleansed from my wounds. I saw all kinds of colors being drawn from my body. Limiting, stagnant thought patterns and beliefs began to flush themselves into the pool. The crystal clear water became murky.

I felt cleansed from the inside out. Fresh, flowing water poured into the pool and it began to feel clear again. I got out of the healing pool, and returned to sit on Solution's lap. The rain clouds had passed.

I drifted, half asleep, to a place that seemed like a realm somewhere beyond this earth plane. Someone asked me if I would like to see my father. I acknowledged that I would. The next moment he was standing before me. We greeted each other much differently than we had on earth. I felt no confusion or fear. I spoke to him from my soul. He listened with interest to what I said.

"Dad, you played the role of my father and I played the role of your son. But these were merely the roles we played in the sojourn of our lives. I forgive you for not being a nurturing father. Life was hard for you because you had your own wounds that created your anger. I know there is a reason we came together. We had something to work out. I feel the hardships of our relationship have now blossomed into a gift. I'm now wiser and have a better understanding of other people's pain. I see you as my spiritual brother and I wish you well on your journey. Trust the wisdom of the universe, be open, and allow the rest to unfold."

He listened intently to every word I said. He was choked with feelings and all he could communicate was, "Thank you." I rested my head on his chest. I knew he had now healed his relationship with me, and I had healed my deepest wounds. Then he dissolved like a vapor mist.

The impact of our resolution was profound. It was as if a healing wave had rippled back through time and touched the wounded hearts of those who had lived in our ancestral line long before my father and me. A painful and self-defeating behavior pattern had been resolved and would no longer be passed on to future generations.

53

I WOKE FROM THE DREAM OF THE WORLD

Wow! I sat up straight. What an experience! A significant energy shift had taken place inside me. My energy body felt light and clean. I was sparkling inside. I felt an immensely powerful connection. I was rooted to the earth, and at the same time, deeply connected to the heavens. Every cell in my body tingled with delight.

I quieted my mind again and entered into the stillness. I felt a warm steaming of delightfully soothing energy flowing from the core of my being. As I sat on Solution's lap, I bathed in the golden inner light gently steaming within me. I understood now what Grandfather meant when he spoke of drinking from the inner well; the eternal stream of the soul.

I heard a still voice speak: You are awake from the dream of the world. My eyes opened wide and I repeated aloud, "I am awake from the dream of the world."

"I'm awake from the trance!" I told Solution and I shouted to the squirrels. I told the setting sun, and I told the trees. I felt them sharing in my celebration. I felt as if the nature around me was an extension of myself, and together we were part of the sacred fabric.

I rested in this bliss for many hours and then slipped off into a deep sleep until sunrise. When I opened my eyes the first thing I became aware of was the steaming process continuing to take place inside me. That warm dance of energy was still bubbling forth from my inner well.

I spent the next couple of days picking berries,

swimming and relaxing in the sun. The flow of energy within me continued feeling vibrant and alive. At night I built a fire and cooked rice and beans. I reflected over my life. As an observer, I witnessed how the journey had brought me to where I was. It all seemed like a dream, and the funny thing is I had believed the dream, never knowing I was in a trance. I was thankful I'd heard my wake-up call and that Grandfather had come into my life. If I had not heard the call, where would I have ended up? I wondered. Surely I would have remained in the trance.

I felt it was time to return to Grandfather. I looked forward to sharing my experience. I asked God to allow me to be an instrument for the highest good, and I said farewell to Solution and the healing pool. I thanked them for their nourishing support and friendship.

I enjoyed a peaceful walk on the way back. This time, none of the fallen branches looked like rattlesnakes. I did see a striped garter snake. I picked her up and she slithered through my fingers. Her tongue darted in and out. I thanked her for helping me conquer my fear of snakes.

54

CONFIRMATION

I approached the waterfall back at Stillpoint at about sunset. I was surprised to find Grandmother Prema had arrived from the city during my absence. She and Grandfather were sitting on the warm rocks with their feet in the water.

"Dillon! Welcome back!" Grandfather called out.

"Hello, Dillon," said Grandmother Prema.

"It's good to see you both," I said.

Grandfather asked if I had seen any snakes on my journey.

"Look out!" I pointed to a stick lying on the ground. "There's one now!" We all laughed.

Grandmother Prema got up and walked up the hill to the cabin. She returned a few minutes later with a birthday cake she had baked. I felt tears come to my eyes as they sang Happy Birthday.

"Dillon, we're celebrating your eighteenth birthday, AND," she said, "we are congratulating you on your waking from the dream of the world!"

"How can you tell?" I asked.

"Your vibration has changed, and so has your voice. You carry yourself with assurance because you have experienced your original self, and you know now you are part of the universal family."

"Dillon," said Grandfather, "I'm glad you remembered my parting words."

"But how do you know I did, Grandfather?"

"When you left to visit Solution you had one eye

open and one eye closed. The eye that was open was the part of you that had partially awakened from the dream of the world, but there was still another part of you in deep trance. Your wounds and your colored lenses were keeping you stuck. In our time together you had glimpses of awakening, but you were not able to pierce the veil. Now you have, and both of your eyes are open. In the dream I had a few nights ago I heard Solution calling you and I saw you awake from the trance. It made me very happy."

"Thank you, Grandfather. I didn't know what I was in for, but Solution helped me face my blocked energy and a new flow of energy began flooding my body. I'm still feeling it. I feel a strong connection to both the heavens and the earth, and the energy combined is creating something like a soothing, steaming combustion inside me."

Grandmother Prema smiled. "You have performed a marriage without even knowing it."

"What do you mean?" I asked.

"I'm referring to the marriage of heaven and earth. Your connection with Mother Earth and your connection to the heavens has created a marriage. The steaming process is the continuous birth of energy generating within you as a result of that union."

"What a great gift!" I said.

"Yes, it is the beginning of an exciting process of inner alchemy, Dillon, which will facilitate your understanding of energy and vibration," said Grandfather. "Letting go of those old wounds released a denseness in your energy body. Over time you will develop an even deeper connection with your soul, and your energy body will continue to refine itself. This refinement process has raised the vibration of your energy body to a much more subtle level. Now your soul is shining with less obstruction. This union of earth energy and uplifting, creative and inspirational energy of the heavens taking place within you is a gift to the planet. As you receive this energy you are free to give, and your capacity to be a vehicle to serve the highest good will continue to increase."

"What an amazing birthday gift!" I said again. "I feel so balanced. Grandfather, are those tears of joy trickling from your eyes?"

"Yes, Dillon. They are joyful tears. I am happy to see your transformation."

"Grandfather Sage has taught you well," said Grandmother Prema. "I couldn't have done better myself," she laughed.

55

LET'S GET REAL

I woke up at daybreak the next morning. My mind began to wander out of control. My summer at Stillpoint was nearly over and I found myself feeling stressed about going back home. I worried that I might get pulled back into my old way of thinking and behaving. The soothing, steaming energy inside me ceased.

I got up and dressed, and taking a basket from the kitchen, crept quietly out of the cabin. Several types of wild berries were in season and I thought I'd surprise Grandfather and Grandmother Prema with some for breakfast. I returned a short time later and found Grandmother Prema in the kitchen, making tea.

"Dillon, they're beautiful. Thank you," she said, taking the basket. "I can tell they were picked with love." I watched as she washed the berries and told her of my apprehensions about going home.

"My soap opera got the best of me," I said.

"Well, Dillon, it did. But that's okay!"

"That doesn't make sense. I experienced freedom. Why go back to bondage?"

"Let's get real, Dillon. Who said your journey is over?"

"You mean it's okay to get pulled back into the trance?"

"I didn't say go into a slumber with both eyes closed, sleeping so deeply that it's hard to wake up. At times you will find yourself going about with one eye open and the other one closed, just like this morning. A part of you got pulled into your self-created drama, but another part of you was aware of your trance."

"You mean it's okay to get dirty as long as you know how to clean yourself off?"

"Yes, Dillon. The reason it's okay is because it's going to happen! It happens to Grandfather, and it happens to me. If we think it's not okay, then we end up arguing with a done deal."

"I see what you mean. That type of thinking is a trance in itself and can pull us deeper into the dream of the world."

"Yes. So rather than belittling yourself for slipping back, just wake up and return to the center of being. Use your open eye to help the eye that's closed to open again. When you're awake from the trances of everyday life, both eyes are open."

"But what if I get so drawn into the drama I can't get out?"

"Did Grandfather talk to you about that 'can't' word? If you think "I can't get out," then you won't. Your intention is 'I will keep my eyes on the light ahead. If I get sidetracked, or caught up in a diversion that takes me off base, I will get back on the main road.' "

"That makes sense. Grandfather says when we focus on what we're afraid might happen, we send energy in that direction, making it more likely to happen. When we focus on positive intention, our energy becomes directed in support of the highest good."

"Right. This is how we create and manifest good things in our lives."

"So, if I get sidetracked . . . "

"Don't you mean 'when' Dillon?" Grandmother Prema smiled.

"When I get sidetracked I'll observe the lesson

before me, return to my center and proceed forward on my journey."

"You are learning to manage your energy, Dillon, and you'll discover what drains your energy. Thinking, emotions, talking and sensory overload are all examples of how our energy gets depleted. Remember this, Dillon: energy is infinite. The key is to replenish your energy faster than it is being exhausted. You will then maintain a healthy reserve. You now have the skills to do this. Enjoy the learning process! With practice, it will become natural and effortless."

"It is nice to hear you two talking," said Grandfather, as he entered the kitchen. "Dillon, you are ready to return to the world. Don't worry. You will have more fun than you've ever had before! It will be a new type of fun, though, because now you understand energy follows intention. Through your positive intention you will manifest a creative life and be of service to others." He became very serious. "Dillon, listen carefully! Do your very best to be aware of where you place your intention. This is the key ingredient in how your journey will unfold."

"I will, Grandfather."

The three of us sat quietly for a few moments. I could feel a flowing dance of energy surrounding us. I felt exhilarated, but grew sad as I thought again about leaving Grandfather and the mountains and the river and Solution.

"Grandfather, I don't know how to say good-bye. Words cannot describe what I feel."

"I understand, Dillon. That is why the depth of our connection is beyond words."

"This feels like my home. I don't feel like leaving."

"Dillon, remember your home is wherever you are. When you live from your inner center, you are always at home."

"I know the universe is my family, but I don't know how to say good-bye to you. I'm not sure I want to say good-bye."

"I appreciate your sincerity and courage, Dillon. Thank you for being my dear spiritual brother. Where you go from here is all part of the plan, just as our summer together was part of that plan. Now you are embarking on a new adventure and I am excited for you. I know you will be of service to life and you will continue to learn and grow through this process."

56

THE JOURNEY CONTINUES

As I was packing my clothes a few days later, I picked up the journal I'd kept over the summer. I turned to the first page. "Welcome to Stillpoint, the classroom of life," Grandfather had said when I'd first arrived. I'd had no idea what he was talking about. Now I knew the stillpoint is my soul. I felt a great love for this land that had served as my teacher in so many ways.

Also at the beginning of my journal were the five principles Grandfather had given me. They were no longer just a theory. I am a soul, and this is the essence of who I am. I am an active participant in life, and my choices determine my momentum. As I cooperate with life, life cooperates with me. Harmony is my true nature.

I sat down on my cot and stared out the window. I felt I'd learned more that summer than I had in all my years of school. Grandfather had told me true education is a synthesis that includes learning the interconnected relationship between parts. Schools often break information down, and fail to integrate learning in a way that is relevant to life.

There is a certain type of trance that develops from the type of education we receive in public school. Life is not a series of fragmented bits of information, but this is the unspoken message we are given during our schooling years.

We become disconnected from understanding and experiencing that everything is connected. We become mentally fragmented as we are forced to memorize facts without understanding the relevance they have to our everyday reality. There is a natural order to life. The unfoldment of events and situations is connected to preceding events. When fragmentation is what we learn, then fragmentation is what we see and experience. We lose our sense of connection to the whole. We perceive separateness rather than unity. And we fail to experience our deep connection with nature.

Grandfather was amazed at how we could finish all our years of schooling without learning what a balanced life is all about. Students leave school without the common sense it takes to manage their own lives. He had laughed at how I knew lots of scientific facts, but didn't know how to fix a leaky toilet.

He was also concerned that students did not learn to think for themselves. The gift of their unique expression was not being cultivated.

I closed my journal and finished packing. I was looking forward to seeing my mom. When she picked me up later that day, I was surprised at how happy she was to see me! It was interesting to be with her. On one hand, I still saw her as my mother, but now I also recognized her as my spiritual sister who shared the main road. She had her path and I had mine.

I used to feel I was locked in a power struggle with her. Now I knew she just had her role to play and was doing the best she could. I will continue to play the role of the son, just as there are many roles to play in life. But I know who I really am is beyond all those roles.

These roles, and the many ways they are played, come and go. They come and go just like thoughts and emotions come and go. I now feel compassion toward myself and life. Who I really am is soul, my original self, who remains the same throughout all time.

When both my eyes were closed, I saw the world only in the way I had been taught and conditioned to see it. My wounds colored my vision. I failed to see how my own conditioning created the fence that kept me corralled. I opened the gate and the road ahead feels wide open.

I know now, when we are in the trance of the world, it's as if there's a special day we are awaiting when all will be perfect. We fail to realize the moment is always here. It never goes anywhere. There is nothing you have to arrive to. The moment is waiting to greet us with joy.

Thank you for taking the time to read my story about how I came to recognize the trances of everyday life and awoke to the deeper spiritual essence of who I am.

I'm glad our paths have crossed. If you're reading these words, it's because it's part of the plan. What I would like to share with you in parting are the words I will always remember: *Trust the wisdom of the universe, be open, and allow the rest to unfold.*

AFTERWORD

The challenges of the new millennium afford each of us the opportunity to take personal responsibility for leading lives filled with compassion, balance and harmony. We are all connected on many levels, therefore our individual healing and growth contributes to universal healing and the wellness of the planet itself. The power of our collective intention is not to be underestimated.

It is my sincere hope that this book will aid you in the exciting journey that lies ahead. Let us join together in a collective intention as we ask for the highest good to manifest itself at all levels of existence.

Ed Rubenstein
April 1999

Cassette Tapes

Ed Rubenstein has produced two guided meditation tapes to assist those readers interested in cultivating the balance, harmony and compassion discussed in *An Awakening From the Trances of Everyday Life: A Journey to Empowerment.*

Releasing, Letting Go, and Creating Space For Change

This cassette tape is designed to assist you with exploring places of tense, frozen or stuck energy and to begin the process of dissolving constricted emotional patterns. This facilitates an expansion of neutral space so there is more room to manifest constructive change in your life.

Centering, Balance and Harmony

This cassette tape is designed to assist you in further working with your intention, feeling the life force, opening a connection to the heavens and the earth, and gathering and storing energy for enhancing your well-being.

Workshops

Ed Rubenstein offers workshops and retreats to integrate and expound upon the concepts and practices explored in this book. Some of the themes are: recognizing and awakening from the trances of everyday life, learning to live life as if each moment mattered, learning to manage your energy, defusing stuck emotional patterns, developing a relationship between intention and energy flow, circulation of life force (chi) through internal energetic pathways (i.e. microcosmic orbit), cultivating your energetic connection with heaven and earth, experiencing your stillpoint, and connecting to your core self. If interested, call (828)649-3870 for details on how a workshop or retreat can be organized for your group or organization.

Visit our Website at: www.sages-way.com

☐   Send me "Releasing, Letting Go and Creating Space for Change." Enclosed is $10.95 plus $3.00 for S&H. NC residents add 6% sales tax.

☐   Send me "Centering, Balance and Harmony." Enclosed is $10.95 plus $3.00 for S&H. NC residents add 6% sales tax.

☐   Send me both tapes for a discount price of $8.95 for each tape plus $3.50 for S&H. NC residents add 6% sales tax. (Additional tapes may be purchased at $8.95 plus 50 cents each tape for S&H.)

☐   Place me on your mailing list for information concerning workshops and future publications/tapes.

Name _____

Address _____

Phone _____ Email _____

Mail this order form with a personal check or money order for tapes to:
Sages Way P.O. Box 31, Marshall, NC 28753

Cassette Tapes

Ed Rubenstein has produced two guided meditation tapes to assist those readers interested in cultivating the balance, harmony and compassion discussed in *An Awakening From the Trances of Everyday Life: A Journey to Empowerment.*

Releasing, Letting Go, and Creating Space For Change

This cassette tape is designed to assist you with exploring places of tense, frozen or stuck energy and to begin the process of dissolving constricted emotional patterns. This facilitates an expansion of neutral space so there is more room to manifest constructive change in your life.

Centering, Balance and Harmony

This cassette tape is designed to assist you in further working with your intention, feeling the life force, opening a connection to the heavens and the earth, and gathering and storing energy for enhancing your well-being.

Workshops

Ed Rubenstein offers workshops and retreats to integrate and expound upon the concepts and practices explored in this book. Some of the themes are: recognizing and awakening from the trances of everyday life, learning to live life as if each moment mattered, learning to manage your energy, defusing stuck emotional patterns, developing a relationship between intention and energy flow, circulation of life force (chi) through internal energetic pathways (i.e. microcosmic orbit), cultivating your energetic connection with heaven and earth, experiencing your stillpoint, and connecting to your core self. If interested, call (828)649-3870 for details on how a workshop or retreat can be organized for your group or organization.

Visit our Website at: www.sages-way.com

☐   Send me "Releasing, Letting Go and Creating Space for Change."
     Enclosed is $10.95 plus $3.00 for S&H. NC residents add 6% sales tax.

☐   Send me "Centering, Balance and Harmony." Enclosed is $10.95 plus $3.00
     for S&H. NC residents add 6% sales tax.

☐   Send me both tapes for a discount price of $8.95 for each tape plus $3.50 for
     S&H. NC residents add 6% sales tax. (Additional tapes may be purchased at
     $8.95 plus 50 cents each tape for S&H.)

☐   Place me on your mailing list for information concerning workshops and
     future publications/tapes.

Name _____

Address _____

Phone _____   Email _____

Mail this order form with a personal check or money order for tapes to:
Sages Way   P.O. Box 31,   Marshall, NC   28753